THE SOBER ADDICT

THE SOBER ADDICT

A Guide on How to Be Functional with
the Dysfunctional Disease of Addiction

DC HYDEN, CASAC-ADV

True 2 Scale Press

Published in the Unites States of America by
True to Scale Press

New York, New York

Library of Congress Cataloging-in-Publication Data

Hyden, Daniel, [October 2019]

The Sober Addict:

Includes index.

ISBN 978-1-7359738-0-7

True 2 Scale Press

Printed in the United States of America

First Edition

To my motivations:

Amaya and **Lailinda** ...

and to those who only focus on the Addict part
of The Sober Addict,

you all motivate me as well.

Contents

"*I learned to recognize the thorough and primitive duality of man; I saw that, of the two natures that contended in the field of my consciousness, even if I could rightly be said to be either, it was only because I was radically both.*"
— Robert Louis Stevenson,
The Strange Case of Dr. Jekyll and Mr. Hyde

Foreword

Is someone you love an addict?

D.C. Hyden, a former addict and now an addiction counselor, aims to spark a more open and honest dialogue about the real role addiction plays in a substance abuser's life and the lives of those, who love him. His goal is to present the reality of life as an addict, and the internal struggle that occurs between the host (the original person) and his "addict-identity" (the person he becomes once the addiction takes over).

D.C. provides the average person with an in-depth look at what it really means to be a drug and alcohol addict in today's world – the stigma, labels, and judgement, along with the challenges that arise when one tries to "get clean" and "stay clean."

He doesn't mix words, which is a good thing. This isn't the time to be nice and politically-correct; rather, it is the time to shine a light on this disease, because it is a disease, one that isn't talked about in its truest sense enough. But, D.C. Hyden's book, The Sober Addict" does just that – talks about it, so we can take action.

It's time we stopped looking at addict, as morally damaged, because that couldn't be further from the truth. These are essential good people, who accidentally took a wrong turn – one that led to addiction. Therefore, they don't need our scorn; they need our understanding and support. They need help.

D.C. explains in his book, "The Sober Addict," that addiction can be overcome by recognizing and understanding the emotional forces underlying addictive behaviors. This book is not only a Godsend for addicts, it's a guide for enablers and helpers (loved ones, who are desperate to "save" their children, spouses, parents, close friends, family members, and anyone else that means the world to them.

And, as a Family Psychologist, I can honestly say this book will be extremely beneficial for those in the addictions field and the counseling field. It's easy to lose touch with the reality of addiction, but "The Sober Addict" reminds us of it through poignant stories and a touch or sarcastic humor. And, guess what? It works.

Therefore, I have no doubt that this book will provide those suffering from addiction and their loved ones with important tools they can use to identify and address the root cause of addiction, the consequences of "using and abusing," and the steps needed to "get sober" and "stay sober." D.C. offers us all a chance to change our mentalities and make a real difference in the lives of drug and alcohol users, abusers, addicts, recovering addicts, and recoverees. We just have to be willing to accept the challenge.

It's a book that everyone should have in their arsenal, because it will change your perspective on addiction, people, and life.

Dr. R. Y. Langham

Family Psychologist

INTRODUCTION

Imagine having to go on a long motorcycle ride while suffering from a painfully annoying hemorrhoid. In the beginning, it doesn't bother you, but as the journey continues, you begin to notice how it's affecting your trip. The itching gets worse and worse - you just want to scratch your ass, but you can't.

As time passes on a seat that feels like a stack of hardcover books, your thoughts and attitude begin change. Your tender hemorrhoid becomes a painful hemorrhoid and, later a bleeding hemorrhoid. What was once an enjoyable experience is now becoming more and more unmanageable with every bump in the road. Hoping it goes it away on its own doesn't work. As your hemorrhoid grows, so does your pain, discomfort, and irritability.

You become miserable and feel like misery is your new state-of-being. You can't do the usual things you used to enjoy, like taking a nice long, relaxing bathroom break to relieve yourself on your favorite toilet. Now, it's just painful bowel movements like you're trying to pass sharp rocks.

Honestly, this previously minor inconvenience is now excruciating. You curse your hemorrhoid and want to get rid of it, but don't know how to. You're curious about your problem, but you don't want to put your fingers down there - it's nasty and embarrassing. It's a sensitive issue, so you can't just tell anyone about it... It's too personal. Just the thought of it is uncomfortable, but you don't want to see a professional about it, so you keep your problem to yourself.

As time passes, your hemorrhoid problem gets worse and worse. Believe me, it's not going away anytime soon. You can mask it and try to forget about it, but it is always there, waiting to flare up. The further you travel with your issue, the less you feel *normal*. You find yourself doing things you said you'd never do, like participating in alternative forms of pain management. All you want to do is relieve your discomfort.

You start to believe you're going to be "stuck" with this problem for the rest of your natural-born life. So, you ask yourself, "What's the point of even seeking treatment?" The truth is you just want the pain to end, but don't know how or where to start. It hurts so much you don't want to continue... but you also don't want to stop. You are at the point now where you can't ignore your problem any longer... It's a pain in the ass!

Well, this scenario mimics what it's like to have an addiction. Frankly, it's a significant pain in the ass, but unlike having a flaming hemorrhoid, addiction can kill you.

As the disease of addiction progresses through its various phases, it becomes a matter of life-or-death. Addiction shreds lives, families, finances, and any other thing we hold dear in life apart. It's a fight for life itself. But, unlike a hemorrhoid problem, addiction is **not** only a personal issue. Those surrounding the addict are also affected by it, suffering through the consequences of it, as well.

All of society feels the impact of addiction, from increases in crime, illnesses, and healthcare costs to picking-up the slack at work, because your unproductive substance-abusing co-workers aren't doing their job. In other words, the people who are *most* affected by addiction aren't always the addicts... It is usually the people closest to addicts that experience *most* of the "effects" of addiction.

Well, the truth is I wrote this book for them. Who are "they?" Well, "they" are the people who reap the unwanted rewards of addiction without even being "high" from "substances." I wrote this book for the people who feel like they need a drink after "dealing" with all of the 'special' issues attached to the addicts in their lives. I wrote this book for those who want to save their addicted loved ones, but don't know how to do it. I feel for all of you because I can relate to your situations. I was once an addict and a clueless "enabler." The truth is, I use to spend my time throwing insults and accusations at the addicts in my life.

This book's goal was to create a guide for both addicts, who are trying to quit, and those already in recovery. I hope this book will help substance abusers who feel that "traditional treatments" aren't for them. I can relate to y'all because I was a "professional addict" for many years. Therefore, this book is also for the "helpers," "enablers," "addicts," and anyone else who is interested in fighting addiction.

Let's start at the beginning. When I was only 5 years old, I had my first taste of a substance of abuse. My father, who always *seemed* so loud and happy, drinking his red and white cans, decided I needed to try it. I *still* remember that first taste so clearly. I swallowed some of it but spat the rest out. What I ingested was acidic, and thus, extremely shocking to my virgin mouth. Truthfully, its taste was similar to the battery acid I used to lick from toy battery tops. The bubbly liquid was harsh, and it stung my mouth, so I quickly spit it out, as much as possible, to the amusement of my father and older sister. Looking back now, I was "hooked" - destined for an addictive future. In other words, that one instance put me on the road to addiction.

Understand that there are things we choose in our lives and things that we don't. In other words, some things are beyond our control. For instance, we can't control who gives birth to us, who raises us, or where we grow up. Having the disease of addiction is beyond the control of millions of people, especially those with substance use disorders (SUDs).

More than half the people suffering from this disorder have one or more genes that predispose them to addiction.[1] I know this from years of research, observations, and counseling services, as a "Credential Alcohol and Substance Abuse Counselor" and "Certified Addiction Recovery Coach." I also know this because my addictions stemmed from a combination of "nature and nurture," a predisposition, and my environment. So, as you can see, my addiction has *always* been a part of me.

To sum it up, we, addicts, didn't *choose* this disease - it *chose* us. It's a part of us, whether we acknowledge it or not. Thus, we need all the help we can get if we want to keep it from killing us. Honestly, addiction is one of the most challenging diseases to treat, and it's even more difficult for an addict to achieve full remission.

I pray this book serves, as a real-world guide, for someone who wants to work his way out of the never-ending cycle of "use and abuse." **Disclaimer**: I like to explain and break down things using dirty biker terms. In other words, I want to be direct and to the point with people. It's just who I am. So, hopefully, I won't come across as borderline crude. Remember that clinically clean advice isn't *always* the best way to fight a dirty disease like addiction.

---

1.   NIDA. (2016). Genetics. Retrieved from https://www.drugabuse.gov/related-topics/genetics

The "helper," "enabler," and "addict" can use my direct advice as tools to break the chains that bind them to drug and/or alcohol abuse. You cannot combat a problem if you don't know what the problem is, so I want to begin by describing, in detail, precisely what addiction is. Chapters in this book will highlight the progressive nature of addiction. The thing is most addicts do not become addicts overnight. In fact, like any other disease, it occurs in progressions and stages. More specifically, addiction has distinct phases, which I will explain, so the "helper" and "addict" will know exactly where they are, and probably where they are going.

After that, I will fully address the mindset of addicts, so you'll have an insider view of the thoughts and actions that drive this problem. When you are an addict, you spend your time fighting an internal conflict with external forces. I will provide more information on this conflict in later chapters. Keep in mind that each chapter builds off the previous one.

I will also explain the cost of addiction in depth and provide you with a gut-wrenching account of how we all pay for this problem. Moreover, I will provide realistic tips on how to **not** pay so much. I want to help you avoid enabling your addicted loved one, so I plan to break all of these things down, similar to how a Kindergarten teacher breaks down the alphabet.

Later in the book, I will delve into ways to motivate yourself or your loved one to achieve sobriety. The purpose of "relapse prevention" is to teach you how to maintain sobriety or help a loved one keep it. In closing, I will describe what it is like to be a "Sober Addict."

I'm just a simple man in recovery, who's lived a not-so-simple life in "use and abuse." Just consider me your "addict insider," taking you for a ride through the various phases of addiction, from its onset to remission, or its eventual end. I was a "professional addict," who could only hold a professional job temporarily. I'd get higher than high and lower than low.

Fortunately, I was eventually able to overcome my drug of choice (DOC). Now, I spend my time teaching addicts, and whoever cares about them, how to **not** lose so much to this disease. Therefore, my ultimate goal is to teach you how to live with, love, and help an addict recover from their addiction. Why? Because addicts that are just as damaged as me CAN be redeemed.

For years, I beat my head against a rock, again and again, wondering why I wasn't getting better. I was restless, irritable, and generally discontented. I was sad and angry that I had put myself in a position to lose so much. The result? More "use and abuse." Honestly, I didn't understand my disorder. As a result, I was determined not to accept it. My life sucked, and I decided to abuse whatever drug I wanted just because my life sucked. However, even though

I abused this-or-that drug, the problem was *still* there. It didn't magically disappear after drugging and drinking.

I heard about treatment options, but they didn't seem to apply to me or my situation. Seeking help for drug abuse was hard because I couldn't relate to the methods of counselors, psychologists, psychiatrists, or social workers. One of the reasons I wrote this book is for the hundreds of clients I've counseled over the years – clients who felt the same way.

As I mentioned above, my goal was to create a self-help guide that both addicts and non-addicts could benefit from. Therefore, my methods are forged in the fire of the consequences of addiction.

I enter places most therapists, social workers, and counselors will not. I meet with my addicted client, where he is - figuratively and literally. Thus, my passion is to help my addicted clients successfully move through the various "stages of change" to prevent their deaths. I also conduct "street interventions," traditional interventions, individual counseling sessions, group sessions, detox referrals, out/inpatient treatment programs, recovery coaching, and relapse prevention exercises.

My experience and education are based on the peer support and clinical service models of substance abuse treatment. I specialize in sober & clean-living strategies. I stuffed all of my "printable" experiences into these 11 chapters. It is based on my life's work as an "all the above" counselor. So, if you're reading this, as a "helper," "enabler," or "addict," you're taking a step in the right direction, and I thank you for doing so.

CHAPTER I

The Disease of Addiction

Instant gratification takes too long.
— Carrie Fisher
1956 - 2016
(Cause of Death: Suspected Drug Overdose)

I'm Sick!

Knowing how an addict thinks can give you better insight into what he will do. So, let's get into the mindset of an addict. This mindset is shared among many of my "brothers" and "sisters," regardless of race, gender, nationality, and socioeconomic status. We all have the same flawed mental processes inhabiting and impairing our ability to stop - regardless of our various DOC. So, who better to detail how these impaired brains function than an "ex-professional addict" with over eighteen-years of "use and abuse" experience?

The truth is you may be dealing with someone, who seems selfish, reckless, irritating, stubborn, disgusting, and even a little "crazy." Possibly this person is just *one* of these things, or perhaps she is *all* of them. This person could be described in several conflicting ways before, during, or af-

22 of page nav>22

ter their substance "use and abuse." Moreover, maybe this person is your family member, spouse, friend, child, or even yourself. It may have been an exceptionally long time since you or your loved one acted "normal." Regardless of the word you use to describe the addict in your life, she should be seen and treated, as you would treat any other sick person in need of help.

This "sickness" has an uncanny ability to make people believe it's not a "sickness," when it really is. This disease makes addicts feel as if it's just a character flaw or this-or-that drug's fault. For instance, when Billy begins stealing from family members and Becky starts turning tricks, it's easy to blame their behavior on a lack of morals or the substance they're trying to obtain.

Billy and Becky may not resemble the person you knew before their "use and abuse," but they are *still* the same person. This "sickness" has just highlighted another aspect of them – one that has always been within. It's not necessarily Billy's and Becky's faults, or even the drugs' fault. It's just that the "sickness" has become a part of them.

Understand that a person with a SUD has just as much control of their illness as a diabetic or cancer patient. All these people need some type of medical assistance for their condition. Sometimes, genetics or lifestyle habits overtime lead to our illnesses, but regardless, once it comes into our lives, there is no cure. What substance abuse professionals, like myself, have learned is that an addict is someone who is "sick" and in need of treatment. The primary and overall presenting problem is addiction.

What Is Addiction?

1.   A Disease

First and foremost, addiction is a neurological (brain) disease. The American Society of Addiction Medicine defines it as "a primary, chronic disease of brain reward, motivation, memory, and related circuitry" (ASAM, 2020).[2]

So, basically, addiction is "primary," meaning that it is not caused by anything else, and it is "chronic," meaning it's long-lasting. It affects the brain's circuits by hijacking biological processes to "reward" us with a hefty dose of dopamine.

2.   NOT a Choice

Do you honestly think your addicted love one wants to f**k – up his life with alcohol and drugs? You can think about it on many different levels (psychologically, religiously, socially, economically, and biologically), but the answer is simple -No. Regardless of the context you use to support your theory, and despite the history of pain your loved one has caused everyone involved, he does not *want* to be a substance abuser. He just doesn't have a choice.

---

2.   American Society of Addiction Medication. (2020) Definition of addiction. Retrieved from https://www.asam.org/for-the-public/definition-of-addiction

- ADDICT INSIGHT -

"ADDICTS DO NOT FREELY CHOOSE ADDICTION – ADDICTION CHOOSES THEM."

I tend to think of things in the most basic terms, and then break them down to the least common denominator. It's a fact that humans are programmed for self-preservation. In other words, one of the most fundamental goals of human nature is to preserve one's own life. As a result, our bodies automatically take safety measures to shield us from harm. We have tons of built-in safety measures from involuntary reflexes like eye blinks to sweating to cool the body down and the fight-or-flight response. However, an "actively abusing addict's" (AAA) desire for drugs and alcohol overrides their survival instincts of self-preservation. We, addicts, are not built like other people. Our ability for self-preservation is faulty, at best.

Of course, humans have free will to make decisions for their lives, just like we can self-preserve. No one forces alcohol down an alcoholic's throat, and no one forces, for the most part, a drug addict to inject heroin into her arm with a dirty syringe. So yes, the addict decides to use it. But it is this "messed-up" decision making that leads us back to the first point of addiction: it's a brain disease. So, if a brain disease affects their ability to make the right decisions for their well-being, how is it their *choice*?

During my years of drinking, drugging, recovering, and counseling, I've yet to meet someone who truly *wants* to get cancer from smoking cigarettes. I also haven't encountered one person who *wants* to develop cirrhosis of the liver due to drinking alcohol. In addition, I haven't met anyone who *wants* to alienate his entire family after stealing everything but the kitchen sink to support his heroin habit. Furthermore, I'm pretty sure not one of my clients *wants* to die from their addiction. So, as you can see, an addict does not freely *choose* addiction – the addiction *chooses* them.

3. A Slow Form of Suicide

Addiction gets progressively worse over time. This chronic "sickness" sucks every iota of life, money, and health from the "infected." There is no degree of well-being while being a substance abuser. Drugs and alcohol destroy your body while also stripping you of your mental health at the same time. As a result, your body and mind are always in jeopardy, placing you in unsafe, risky, and dangerous situations. The more you use, the higher your chances of losing your life to this disease's consequences.

More specifically, every drink, smoke, or pill popped brings you closer to an untimely death. There are millions of deadly circumstances that could play out in "use and abuse." In other words, the substance could directly cause an overdose, substance-related injuries from a car accident, or even death. In 2017, drug-related deaths reached epidemic proportions. In fact, more people died of drug-related reasons that year than military deaths in the Vietnam War (National Center for Health Statistics. 2018).[3] Then, there are outside factors like drugs that cause you to place yourself in unsafe environments – i.e., where drugs, drug dealers, drug money, and drug violence can be found.

Understand that most people who become addicted don't die after their initial use. Instead, they die after years of "use and abuse." It typically occurs after you build a tolerance and become complacent with your drug of choice. Or, you "get clean" for a short amount of time, then relapse. But, because your body can't handle what you have become accustomed to, you overdose. As you probably know from dealing with your addicted loved, as an addict's tolerance for her DOC increases, her control over her actions, or lack thereof, decreases.

Remember, addiction is a disease, not a *choice*. As a result, an addict is tricked into taking an active role in her death – one-hit-at-a-time. Many of us know what it *feels* like to be doing something we know is wrong, but we do it anyway. The same can be said about addiction; however, in this case, we become slaves to a "Higher Power" – drugs and

3. Ahmad, F. B., Rossen, L. M., Spencer, M. R., Warner, M., & Sutton, P. (2018). Provisional drug overdose death counts. National Center for Health Statistics.

alcohol. It is essential to understand that an addict doesn't "use and abuse" drugs or alcohol because she likes danger; instead, she "uses and abuses" because her mind craves the "high" that comes from increased dopamine in the body.

4. A Conflict

Countless parents, spouses, friends, children, and other concerned parties have complained to me that their addicted loved ones "act" as if they're possessed. I have also met just as many AAAs, who swear they are possessed by some "demonic force," outside of themselves, that compels them to do the things they do. At times I feel like my clients and their families want me to perform an exorcism on them or their loved ones.

Consider the parallels between substance use disorders (SUD) and demonic possession. An unknown "force" takes hold of a person and battles for supremacy from the inside out. This "force" struggles with all that is right and decent in the person, at times taking over and creating a totally different version of him. As a result, the "force" becomes a conflict from within, a fight with something that's both foreign and native.

Let me reiterate; addiction is an internal conflict - with external factors. It's no coincidence that there are real similarities between addiction and possession. We already know this disease takes control of its victim, giving him no choice, while also slowly killing him as it progresses.

The victim unwillingly relinquishes control, often under the false pretense that he is still in control. Conflict arises from this fight for power. As the "force" or "demon" battles the victim, he weakens and loses himself along the way. In the end, the old version of the person no longer exists, a new "sick" version gains control. This scenario sounds like every possession movie I've ever watched!

The internal factor is the conflict of "war" raging inside the addict, and the external factor is his DOC. The fight isn't against cocaine, heroin, alcohol, or pills – rather, the *real* battle is against the addict and person who does not *want* to be an addict.

Thereby, addiction is already pre-made for those who are predisposed to it. The drugs just release another version of the person – one that has been lying dormant. This internal conflict is hard to fight because it's a heavyweight prize bout with competing factors taking place in the addict's mind with the stakes being life-or-death. In other words, this conflict takes place in a mind that's already behind the eight-ball.

It's All About the Dopamine Baby!

An addict's brain craves the neurotransmitter, dopamine. Scientists have mapped a reward highway in our minds, and this transmitter is the sexy new Harley on that road. Dopamine plays a critical role in the rewarding effects of brain stimulation, psychomotor stimulants, opiates, and food (Wise, 1989).[4] Depending on the person, it gives us a pleasurable rush, euphoria, and a safe and warm feeling. The addictive drug releases excessive amounts of dopamine, creating the desired effect, and reinforcing the need for continued use.

The drugs fueling the addiction are both *rewarding* and *reinforcing*. Addicts receive pleasurable feelings (a reward) from the drug(s), and the "use and abuse" reinforces the addictive behavior, encouraging it to continue. It's truly a vicious cycle. Pleasure-seeking quickly turns into pleasure-compulsion - compulsion towards drugs and alcohol. The compulsion, in turn, leads to abuse and increased tolerance. At the same time, mental and physical dependency takes hold.

It's still scary, but interesting to hear my clients tell me they think and feel exactly as I did when I was actively using. During those days, I was never satisfied, always restless, constantly uneasy, and unable to feel fulfilled. I remember feeling the lyrics from that U2 song, "I still haven't found what I'm looking for..."

The drugs had hijacked my pleasure center and nothing, but my good old DOC would satisfy me. The thing is when tolerance sets-in, it takes more and more to feel the

4.   Wise, R. A., & Rompré, P. P. (1989). Brain dopamine and reward. Annual Review of Psychology, 40, 191-225.

pleasurable effects. Like the lyrics in Guns & Rose's song, Mr. *Brownstone*, "My lil got more and more…"

The truth is I always had to have more because more was the only way to prolong my "high." Being "high" resembled the feeling of "puppy love," while walking on cloud-nine in perfect Hawaii weather, after eating a delicious 5-star meal. But, even when I didn't get my "fix," I continued to drink and drug, and sooner or later, it would come.

There is an adage that says that addiction is passed down from one generation to the next. It goes like this, "One is too many, and a thousand is never enough." The reason this adage gets passed around like blunt on 4/20 is that it's true. Like the badges cops carry around with them on patrol, an addict also carries a badge with her only it's a badge of "non-self-regulation." In other words, addicts cannot "self-regulate" once they lose control, and this lack of control begins in the brain.

Research suggests that dopamine is an internal motivator for the addict's mindset and external actions. It's simple but very complicated. The "reward pathway ride" leads to a reward-dictating mindset *and* mindset-dictating behavior.

Thus, my goal with this chapter is to describe the common mindsets of those with SUDs, and the actions that "ride shotgun" with them. I believe that by recognizing impulsive, manipulative, and ritualistic mindsets, you can change addictive behavior for recovery.

More Than a Feeling

Impulsivity is like a powerful V Twin motor delivering an addict to immediate gratification. The initial thought of someone with a SUD is to act on his or her desire to use. Biologically, addicts are more impulsive than the general population, due to prefrontal cortex deficiencies. This portion of the brain acts as a median between the pleasure center and reason. Therefore, addiction is likely due, in part, to increased impulsiveness that comes from a loss of the frontal cortical inhibition of impulses (Crews/Boettiger, 2009).[5] More specifically, positive associations attach to drug use, while negative associations attach to "periods of abstinence."

Honestly, acting on impulse came naturally to me. What I wanted to do, I did, whenever I damn-well pleased. This pattern got worse as I aged because I had no one but myself to hold me accountable. My addiction thrived in my lifestyle. Anytime I wanted to drink, I did with impulsivity. I got accustomed to fulfilling my cravings, as they happened, but this put me deeper into an abusive pattern.

I've been called so many names as an alcoholic, but the most dead-on was "hard-headed." It took me years of hard knocks to even realize I had an impulse-control problem. This lightning bolt hit me one morning while I was in my

---

5. Crews, F. T., & Boettiger, C. A. (2009). Impulsivity, frontal lobes and risk for addiction. Pharmacology, Biochemistry, and Behavior, 93(3), 237-47.

job's locker room. The day before, I had decided to drink during my lunch break - which then led me to "happy hour drinking" after work - which led to jumping on my motorcycle and going to the liquor store for a "pre-bar drink," - which led to me to another bar for a "social drink" - which led to me taking the bartender home to have "unprotected sex" - which led me to go to work the next morning with a hell of a hangover, and smelling like sex and alcohol. I was acted on impulse, doing precisely what I wanted to do, but I was not in control.

Impulse-control is now a focus of substance abuse treatment, but you will need to be the human version of this treatment to help your loved one.

You must recognize impulsive behaviors, so you can hold your addicted loved one accountable for identifying and regulating her behaviors. Try to offset any impulsive actions by bluntly explaining to your loved one how his actions are negatively affecting others. In other words, make him feel guilty because accountability is the key.

Manipulation

Addicts are master manipulators. With a biological lack of impulse-control, we "users and abusers" manipulate any and all situations, so the outcome yields the desired substance.

```
- ADDICT INSIGHT -

"I GOT SO GOOD AT VERBAL
MANIPULATION THAT I WOULD MAKE
MY FAMILY AND GIRLFRIEND
FEEL GUILTY FOR NOT LETTING ME DRINK."
```

Q&A

Question: Who are addicts best at manipulating?

Answer: They are *best* at manipulating those who care the most about them.

Question: How do addicts manipulate those who care most about them?

Answer: By using their family's and friend's compassion, guilt, and love against them.

Question: How can someone avoid being manipulated by an addicted love one?

Answer: To be continued...

The phrase, "You can't always get what you want," has no real-world application in the minds of those with SUD. We will get what we want by any means necessary. The addicts I know, myself included, are some of the most determined people on the planet. If only we could put forth the same effort in life, as we do in getting "high," we'd be the most productive people in the world.

I digress; let's get back to the last question and its answer.

The key to not being taken advantage of by an addicted loved one's manipulation is paying attention to their words. An addict hurts people through their words. Someone once asked, "How do you know when an addict is lying?" The response, "Whenever they're talking."

But that isn't true, because we use a combination of truth, lies, threats, and promises to manipulate others verbally. Time-after-time, I was able to gain an advantage over others through my words – the right words with the right people. And, because I was so good at doing this, I could drink when I wanted to. I got so good with my verbal manipulation that I'd make my family and girlfriend feel guilty for not letting me drink.

The irony? Even *I* have been taken advantage of through the words of another addict. My crack/cocaine-addicted sister has verbally manipulated me countless times. She has gotten quite good at using the right words to ask me for money for her DOC. Every part of me feels sorry for her and wants to believe she wants to do better, but 97% of the time, she just tries to take advantage of my love. Only when I recognized her manipulative actions did I stop giving her money and feeling like an ass.

So, let's back to the last question...

Question: "How do you avoid being manipulated by your addicted love one?"

Answer: To stop the verbal manipulation, you have to objectively consider your loved one's actions and not just their words.

This is done by taking into account your loved one's past. Why? Well, because it is the best indicator of her future actions. Using past actions as a frame of reference, you can effectively combat verbal manipulation or manipulation by words. When a substance abuser utters the words "I will," "I promise," "I swear," your internal bullshit detector should *code red*, alerting you. Addict's use these loaded words to break down your defenses. So, use them to help you remember the countless times your addicted loved one used the same words to verbally manipulate you to get what she wanted.

Ritualistic

Addicts are creatures of ritualistic habits. Our actions and behaviors are dictated by an innate association between pleasure and our DOCs. In the brain of someone with a SUD, learned environmental cues and rituals become connected to "use and abuse." Throughout my drinking career, I had many rituals that, at the time, I felt enhanced my "high."

During college, in Georgia, this consisted of driving to the county line (Georgia Southern University was located in a dry county where no liquor was sold) and planning how to get girls drunk before I got "wasted" because being "wasted" alone was no fun. It also involved sneaking away from work to go to a nearby liquor store, drooling over the whiskey and beer combinations. However, my all-time favorite ritual was jumping on my motorcycle, riding to the liquor store, getting my favorite alcoholic beverages, going to a park, and sitting in the sun while getting drunk and banging out to 90's rock music.

I made so many liquor store/park trips I couldn't even start my bike by the time I was finished. But, if I could have started it, I wouldn't have gotten very far. The park was my home many nights, but I was a real danger to others, my bike, and myself when I was on the road intoxicated.

Understand that an addict develops rituals over time, and these rituals are clues to their habits. In other words, to get the information you need to recognize these signs, you must pay attention. If you pay attention to your addicted loved one's rituals, you can try to stop them before becoming ingrained in your loved one's life.

In school, I learned something I already knew from the streets - there are stages of addiction. The stages are experimentation, regular use, misuse, abuse, and dependency/addiction. Stage two involves rituals. So, to help yourself or an addicted loved one, you have to place roadblocks in the path of these destructive rituals, as soon as you recognize them. This can be exhausting, but no one said this was going to be easy. *Be nosy, observe, ask questions, and disrupt.* This is serious and can quickly progress into other phases until it is a matter of life-and-death.

Phases of Addiction

There is a ton of credible research on how the disease of addiction progresses. From Jellinek, who initially chose the "phases of alcoholism" to Bador, who originally determined the various "alcoholic types." Based on my own "use and abuse," my observations of other addicts through the years, and the information provided to me by my clients, I've made my own designations for the "phases of addiction."

1. Experimentation Phase

This phase starts off innocent enough. A person decides to experiment with alcohol or drugs due to curiosity or peer pressure. Most people do not progress past this phase. However, at this point, those with a vulnerability towards SUDs have reached a point-of-no-return. But those vulnerable to addictions only represent a subset of the general population.

According to a recent study, there is a strong association between personality traits and addictive behaviors

(Davis and Loxton 2013).[6] Results suggest that once a person, who is predisposed to addiction, takes his first sip or uses a particular drug or substance, he is already past the point-of-no-return.

2. Social Phase:

During this phase, drinking and drugging are done around others, as a means to socialize, fit-in, or relieve social anxiety or stress. Keep in mind that many people use legal and illegal substances for pleasure without developing an addiction. The thing is, in most cases, those without SUDs or other contributing factors **do not** progress past this phase. It is also during this time that a substance user acquires his or her drug of choice. An *internal conflict* marks this phase as to whether to use drugs or abstain from them.

3. Anti-Social Phase:

Here is when a "substance user" becomes a "substance abuser." During this phase, addiction begins to win the internal struggle. Now, the intent is to achieve drink and drug intoxication. In other words, your addicted love one becomes preoccupied with maintaining her "high." *Negative consequences* mark this phase.

---

6.   Davis, C., & Loxton, N. J. (2013). Addictive behaviors and addiction-prone personality traits: Associations with a dopamine multilocus genetic profile. Addictive Behaviors, 38, 2306-2312.

The intensity and frequency of the "use and abuse" places the substance abuser in compromising situations. In fact, a direct result of actions used to gain one's DOC is often criminal.

One's tolerance for her DOC also increases during this phase. The truth is there are specific symptoms (i.e., increased tolerance) an addict **must** exhibit, during a twelve-month period, to be diagnosed with a "substance use disorder." During this phase, SUDs are classified as either mild or moderate.

4. Advanced Phase:

The truth is substance abusers hone their skills and knowledge – skills acquired from the drug culture. The result? ...The creation of a "professional addict." Dependency on one's DOC causes a loss of control in his life. This phase is marked by *disarray*. A person may admit he has an "addiction problem," but take no *real* steps to combat it. Also, an addict's relationships, health, and finances may begin to break down, as the consequences of his actions become more severe.

As time goes on, the addict's tolerance will continue to increase; however, his social status and employment will continue to decrease. During this phase, the "substance use disorder" is often moderate or severe. At this point, an addict *still* has hope of regaining control of his life.

5. End Phase:

During the End Phase of addiction, the addict only cares about obtaining and using her DOC. She is now entirely dependent on drugs or alcohol. At this point, the addict has two choices - use or face withdrawal ("dope sickness" for opioid addicts/DTs = tremors and the "shakes" for alcoholics). In other words, the addict has lost all control of her behavior to the substance or habit.

During this time, the addict loses hope and gives up the fight against her addiction. Personal safety, hygiene, and physical well-being no longer matter to her. Also, during this phase, the criterion for "substance use disorder" is severe. Without treatment, the addict mostly certainly faces death.

6. Remission Phase:

The Remission Phase involves either short-term or long-term abstinence from substances of abuse. During this phase, the disease **does not** progress due to voluntary or involuntary abstinence/sobriety. Voluntary abstinence relies on self-correction during the treatment period, the "cold turkey" method, or both.

Involuntary abstinence may be due to incarceration or a medical condition. During this time, a recoveree enters the "sober process," where he addresses the addiction and makes a sincere attempt to achieve sobriety. Understand

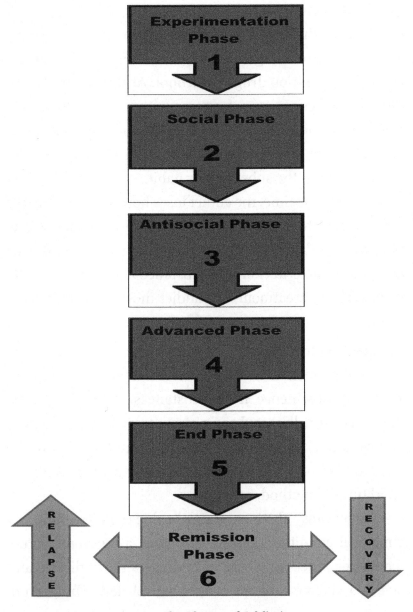

Fig. 1-1: The Phases of Addiction

that he may also relapse, during this phase, returning to previous phases.

Sad But True

Addiction is a sinkhole of a problem, but fortunately, there are many ways to treat it. As with any chronic illness, treatment is a long-term process. If you really want to help your addicted love one or even yourself (if you're an active drug abuser/drug addict), you need to think of this problem, first and foremost, as a "sickness." Next, you need to consider how this "sickness" makes an addict think and act.

Understand that an addict lives in an internal conflict with himself, leading to external conflicts with others. This conflict lead to the most common mindset of an addicted person.

When I was abusing, my actions were definitely impulsive, manipulative, and ritualistic, similar to the actions of every addict I've ever met. Another sad but true fact is that addiction stunts mental growth. So, as an AAA moves through the "Phases of Addiction," the DOC takes control of his thoughts and actions. It doesn't matter if the addict is young or old; he is still a-risk for delayed mental development and mental regression.

You may have also noticed that the addict in your life has a juvenile mindset that causes him to make "child-like" decisions. In part, this is due to the addiction taking control of the person at the onset of maturity. This prevents an addict from growing and maturing naturally. During this time, an addict's decision-making process also becomes stunted, causing him to engage in ill-conceived actions.

In other words, an addict's mindset is manifested through his actions and defined by his words. The truth is we, "user and abusers," leave a trail of toxic waste in our wake, similar to how a careless garbageman goes from home-to-home, dropping litter behind him. Honestly, it doesn't matter if it's your spouse, child, lover, or roommate - you can't trust the words of an addict, especially when you've witnessed behaviors to the contrary. Again, the addict's past actions are the best indicators of their future actions. Their true intentions are exhibited through his actions.

It's difficult to gauge the actions of a conflicted person. I get it. A conflicted person is unpredictable, and thus, liable to do almost anything. Doesn't that sound just like an addict? But if there is something you can trust in your addicted love one's actions or words is that she is wrought with conflict. Ironically, however, in some ways, this conflict is critical. It's this conflict that finally shows an addict that she is indeed an *addict*.

So, if you want to help your addicted love one achieve sobriety, you have to acknowledge the conflict within her and accept that her actions are **not** the product of a "normal" decision-making brain. Think of it this way – an addict suffers from a progressive neurological (brain) disease, literally trying to kill him. It is a disease that is battling for control and making him believe he or she has a say in the matter. Therefore, you must recognize the dual nature of an addict.

CHAPTER 2

The Duality of Addiction

*I guess happiness is not a state you want to be in
all of the time.*

/

Why can I not get some pleasure for myself?
— John Belushi
1949 - 1982
(Cause of Death: Combined Drug Intoxication)

The Struggle Is Real

What do *Dr. Jekyll* and *Mr. Hyde*, *David Banner* and
the *Hulk*, and *Bruce Wayne* and *Batman* have in common
with your "everyday addict?" Well, they *all* struggle with alter egos that *could* end their very existences. For instance,
Dr. Jekyll battles his alter ego, *Mr. Hyde*, to control of their
"shared life." *David Banner* wrestles with the *Hulk* for supremacy of their shared "state of being." And *Bruce Wayne*
clashes with his alter ego, *Batman*, over which persona is
just and should continue. Like these fictional comic book
characters, addicts are in constant conflict with their "addict alter egos," a conflict fueled by their DOCs.

To call *living* with an addiction, a struggle is an understatement. The truth is it's the *ultimate struggle*, an internal battle to the death. In this scenario, a person may want to live, but *struggle* against the part of herself that wants to "take over." Imagine being separated into two pieces – the left and right side of your body. Your left hand is raised, trying to protect itself from your right hand's swinging knife. In essence, *both* sides of the body want to live while being fully in control; however, they know to be in control; the other side must die.

Now, imagine fighting in a 12-round boxing match with yourself, beating yourself up until you are a bloody mess. You taste the warm, salty blood as it slides down your face. Blood that is coming from your self-inflicted jabs to your body. This same fight can be applied to addiction. The "fight of addiction" involves a combination of internal conflict and the external factors I mentioned in Chapter 1.

The truth is an addict's struggle does not lie solely in his or her drug habit; rather, it resides within himself or herself. In other words, addicts consist of two conflicting parties - the person they are *and* their "addict-identities." It is essential to understand that as the addiction progresses, the addict loses control and becomes a host. It is at this time when the "addict-identity" takes over.

The "addict-identity" is not only an internal disease but also an outward manifestation of the addiction itself. Thus, the "drug addict" is genuinely a dual person. What is duality? It is a term commonly used in mathematics, science, philosophy, psychology, and many other fields to signify two separate parts or two versions of something or someone.

To amass the various definitions of duality, and put them in the simplest terms, it involves having a "dual nature" or two-fold. In other words, addiction consists of two distinct versions of the same person. These two versions co-exist in a combative nature. So, rather than being complementary versions of the same person, they are essentially opposing forces.

Keep in mind that although, many people have a "duality" to them (two parts of themselves), the difference between a person with a substance abuse problem and one without it, is that a person with the substance abuse prob-

- ADDICT INSIGHT -

"MANY PEOPLE HAVE A "DUALITY" TO THEM (TWO PARTS OF THEMSELVES), THE DIFFERENCE BETWEEN A PERSON WITH A SUBSTANCE ABUSE PROBLEM AND ONE WITHOUT IT, IS THAT A PERSON WITH THE SUBSTANCE ABUSE PROBLEM IS STRUGGLING WITH ONE SIDE THAT IS LITERALLY TRYING TO KILL HIM OR HER"

lem is struggling with one side that is literally trying to kill him or her.

My struggle with my "addict-identity" was very real. The addict part of me tried to kill me several times, but I did not realize it until it was almost too late. It was the "addict" in me that told me that it was okay for me to get behind the wheel of a car. The result? A horrific accident that twisted my car up into a ball. I wouldn't have been able to get out of my car had it not been for firefighters, who cut me out of it. Because of my traumatic injuries, my brain began to swell and bleed. So, because my "addict-identity" told me it was okay for me to get behind the wheel of my car, while *high*, I gravely injured myself and could have injured or killed someone else. But even though it was my "addict-identity" that *caused* the accident, I was still a willing participant, because I went along for the ride anyway. Honestly, I believe a small part of me *wanted* to drink and drug that night, however a more significant part of me did not want to total my $40,000 car in a near-fatal car accident.

Moreover, it was the "addict" in me that led me to the *wrong* bar in the *wrong* part of town with the *wrong* people one night. I still can't fully remember all of the details of that night, however, based on the information I later obtained from the bartender and police, I was behaving like the *Incredible Hulk* in a place that was known to be a gang hangout. Truth-be-told, at the time, neither me nor my "addict-identity" was aware that the bar was a haven for gang activity.

But, one thing that quickly became apparent is that neither I nor my "addict-identity" was a match for the five guys, caught on the surveillance camera, stomping me into the floor. That night, I walked away from the fight with facial stitches, a broken nose, two black eyes, and an orbital fracture. Although, it probably would have been much worse had I not been in a public place. Once I got a chance to see myself in the mirror, I was shocked. I looked even more battered than after my car crash, which caused my coupe to wrap around a utility pole.

Picture the *Humpback of Notre Dame* with a pepperoni pizza face. Yep, that was me.

So, once again, it was the "addict" part of me that almost got me killed. How?

Well...

- ❖ By speeding through public streets on my motorcycle, while *high*
- ❖ By fist-fighting with strangers, friends, bouncers, cops, and bikers, while *high*
- ❖ By entering homes that looked like mine, but were not, while *high*
- ❖ By walking into traffic with vehicles zooming past me, while *high*
- ❖ By jumping off a balcony, while *high*

❖ By committing other depraved acts of self-destruction, while *high*

I didn't ask for any of that shit to happen and wouldn't have done any of it under normal circumstances... The truth is I went along for the ride because I had no choice, or better yet, because I didn't *know* I had a choice. Ironically, in the movies and comic books, protagonists often get to decide if or when their antagonist alter egos appear. But, ironically, those who are addicted to drugs and alcohol don't get that luxury. In other words, we are unable to control the addicted part of us. The sad part is, most of the people around us don't believe that.

Loved ones, friends, co-workers, and society, in general, typically believe the worst things about addicts – their liars, thieves, etc. They believe what they see and what they see are the "bad things" we do - the ugly, dirty rotten scoundrel parts entrenched inside *every* user-abuser.

At first, we are unaware of this second part of us (duality), but as our substance abuse escalates, the "hidden addict" within us becomes "blinding" like an overly-lit Broadway stage. It is during this time that we become thoroughly acquainted with our "addict" counterparts. More specifically, we are *forced* to come face-to-face with our "addict-identities" after experiencing the life-altering consequences of trauma, change, and isolation.

Thus, me and those closest to me, have gotten to know my "addict-identity" much better after each subsequent self-inflicted trauma. In other words, those closest to me have witnessed the similarities between my "addict-identity" and the fictional characters, *Dr. Jekyll* and *Mr. Hyde*, so much so that I have acquired that nickname from them. Surprisingly, my "sober-identity" is introverted – i.e., respectful and dependable; however, my "addict-identity" is the polar opposite – i.e., loud, obnoxious, reckless, and dangerous.

I know I probably sound like an old alcoholic aunt, a meth-head mom, a crack-fiend friend, or a heroin-crazed husband – one of the stigmatized "undesirables" in society. I get it. I know I probably sound like every other "addict" you've heard about or met from New York to LA. But, this duality is readily observed in *all* of its sufferers.

Still, there is one sufferer; in particular, I want to focus on next. This client's case study provided me with invaluable information and a more in-depth understanding of duality in addicts.

The Curious Case of *Bruce Banner* & His "Addict-Identity"

My client's name isn't really Bruce Banner; however, for confidentiality *and* easier name pronunciation, I decided to change it. I chose Bruce Banner because this client reminds me of *Bruce Wayne, David Banner,* and the *Hulk,* which is why Bruce Banner seemed like an obvious choice. Bruce is a tall, mild-mannered Caucasian male in his mid-forties. And, by American societal standards, he is handsome. He is six-foot-tall with blond hair and blue eyes framed with studious glasses that make him look like a middle-aged *Clark Kent.*

Bruce Banner was raised in an upper-middle-class home on the Upper Westside of Manhattan. His grandparents had money, which is why his family lived in such a prestigious area. His grandparent's money financed Bruce's $50,000k-a-year prep school education at the Lawrenceville School in Jersey. His parents struggled to maintain the status quo, but they were not wealthy like most of the families around them. Bruce was the middle child and often in the middle of his family's dysfunction. There was no history of addiction on either side of his family; however, there was still plenty of bickering and fighting. Money issues eventually led to his parent's divorce. This time was also when Bruce's father began to verbally and emotionally abuse Bruce.

But Bruce's intelligence helped him become prosperous once he became an adult. More specifically, it helped him earn an academic scholarship to NYU with his charming demeanor taking care of the rest.

Then, he charmed his way into a young NYC socialite's life and married into *real* money. The truth is Bruce didn't need his wife's money because his esteemed job as a financial trader at the Deutsche Bank earned him a lucrative annual salary. He was living the "American Dream," but no one, including his ex-wife, was fully aware of Bruce's disease until after the ink on the marriage certificate had dried.

During my first encounter with Bruce, I witnessed first-hand his internal conflict. He stumbled into my office at the treatment center, smelling like week-old sun-dried garbage. His first words to me were, "Hey, I need help. Do you guys still help people here, because I was here before, but I want to come back, because I don't like me, and I want help again..." He said all of that with a cup of vodka on the rocks in his right hand. The "old version" of him wanted help, but his "addict-identity" wanted to drink his life away or die trying. I also learned that Bruce had sunken too deep dark depths right after rising to the pinnacle in his professional and personal lives.

Disclaimer: I could not include all of Bruce's depraved acts while intoxicated, so I will focus on the conflict within him.

Throughout our client/counselor relationship, I felt like I was his personal referee battling between the person who wanted to recover and the addict, who was desperate to take over.

The same man, who had been slapped with a restraining order for threatening to kill his ex-wife on multiple occasions, was always calm when he showed up for group-therapy with a *New York Post* and donuts for his fellow group therapy members in-tow. In other words, Bruce was choirboy respectful, using "Sir" and "Ma'am" in the group. However, when drunk, he'd addressed the treatment staff, police, doctors, and paramedics with every profanity in the book, from f-bombs to racial slurs. According to Bruce's family, he saved his most venomous comments for them.

When he was intoxicated, he'd spew vile remarks at them. For instance, he once told his heartbroken mother to jump into the East River with a cinderblock chained to her because she refused to give him cash for drugs. His ex-wife also mentioned several times, in which Bruce said he'd have their teenage son shove a lit firecracker into her vagina for some imagined wrong she committed against him. Then, there was the time Bruce told his father to suck an HIV-infected dildo because he told his adult son to grow up.

I genuinely believe Bruce said these nasty things to his family as retaliation for the hurtful things they said to him over the years. In fact, after studying Bruce for a while, I determined he was externalizing the emotional and verbal abuse he received from his father and ex-wife. In other words, Bruce was trying to "overachieve" or move past the dysfunction he had experienced for most of his life. Unfortunately, however, he had never learned the necessary coping skills to function properly – i.e., cope with challenges. I also learned that Bruce's siblings also experienced the dysfunction, but none of them developed SUDs.

Bruce was a special case because he was a walking-and-talking contradiction. This man, who looked and smelled like NYC's Most Eligible Bum, sleeping on a heating grate outside of a multimillion-dollar Park Ave building, was the same one who proudly professed he was "too good" to sleep inside of city shelters. The truth is his stench was so strong, it invaded the common areas and traveled up one's nostrils, yet, he still managed to "talk down" to my other clients, as if his "shit didn't stink." The condescending comments that oozed out of his mouth were nauseating, choking the life out of the room during group sessions.

You see, Bruce believed that he was still a financial trader, so he made it a point to lecture the other addicts on the stock market. Yet, the truth was - he was now "homeless addict Bruce," stumbling over his words and always prepared to fight when other addicts called him out on his contradictions. His arrogance not only "empowered" the addict in him, but it also kept him from moving forward in treatment.

Bruce was being treated by an interdisciplinary team the consisted of doctors, nurses, therapists, counselors, and psychologists. Sill, after several unsuccessful months, it was decided that he needed to return to detox and inpatient treatment for the 8th time! Truth-be-told, I experienced that "defeated-relationship-breakup feeling," as I reluctantly signed his discharge papers. Next step? Detox and a higher level of care.

Truthfully, counseling Bruce was challenging, mainly because he often arrived at the counseling sessions above the legal limit of intoxication. He told me he had to drink to avoid shaking like a shopping cart with a bad wheel. **Note**: Alcoholic "shakes" are called "delirium tremens" or DTs. After sleeping on the sidewalks of Manhattan, Bruce would grab several cups of vodka to get himself "going" in the mornings, and then stumble into my office drunk-as-a-skunk. His "addict-identity" had taken over, and that was his new "normal." I never knew which Bruce was going to show up on any given day because the duality of his addiction made him resemble a human light switch with a completely different "addict persona" turning on after a few cups of vodka. However, for those (like his family and ex-wife), who knew him on a deeper, more personal level, his addiction was more sinister than it appeared.

A Real-Life Exorcist

Bruce's family was like countless others, who found it hard to process the duality of addiction. It's easier for some people to think of their loved ones as being "possessed" by a demonic entity than accepting the truth. From this stand-point, a beloved family member was "normal" one day, but a totally different "evil" entity the next. These families can't understand how their precious "Billys" or "Beckys" could morph into "something" so unlike themselves or de-viate from their previous pristine images. The only possi-ble reason for Billy's or Becky's drastic changes from the "All-American" good kids to something dark and "evil" was the presence of some "demon," which is controlling them.

The truth is families, the criminal justice system, schools, and even some churches have compared drugs addicts to people possessed by "evil spirits." These people call addicts "monsters." In their minds, the only rational explanation for the change in their loved one's behavior is that a "monster" has possessed her, causing her to engage in "monstrous acts." When this happens, they unknowing-ly ignore their own enabling behaviors that helped develop that "monster."

Ready for a history lesson? Well, the earliest cultures believed that "possessions" were diseases of the body and mind. These infirmities were caused by "sickness demons" that indiscriminately *chose* humans to persecute on a whim (Biggs, 1995).[7]

---

7. Biggs, R. D. (1995). Medicine, surgery, and public health in Ancient Meso-potamia, Vol. New York, 1911-1924.

Some of these "demons" spread "sickness" based on a person's evil deeds. You see, back in those times, the primitive mind could only explain the unexplainable as *supernatural.* If the illness wasn't a result of the paranormal, then it was from a moral failure, but the fundamental belief was that whatever "it" was, it was still beyond a person's control. Even today, society views addicts as being "possessed" by "evil" drugs because they have flawed morals.

"Possession" and addictions have undeniable similarities. This "alien force" takes up residence in someone, and "claims" the addiction like a dog "claims" its favorite fire hydrant. This "force" struggles with what is right and decent within the person, gaining more strength, as "it" gains more control. Once "it" has the person in "it's" grasp, a new identify forms – one that is entirely different than the "host's" original identity. This is the premise of just about every "possession" movie I've ever seen.

Well, most addiction stories begin the same way.

An addict's head may not rotate 360-degrees as Linda Blair's did in the *Exorcist;* however, he tends to look just as bad. For example, sunken-in eyes surrounded by dark circles, a pale ruddy completion highlighted by open wounds, and a dry mouth filled with rotten teeth under chapped lips. If you don't believe me, *Google,* before and after drug addict images.

Involuntary "demonic possession" is similar to when drug addicts make voluntary decisions. It could even be said that the drugs and alcohol release something within the person – something that has lain dormant for a long time, maybe even since birth. This "demonic entity" or DOC is often blamed for creating the addiction. Why? Well, because as the "addictive force" takes over, a new "addict-identity" is unleashed. This new identity has been there the whole time, just waiting for a chance to "escape."

It's fascinating how someone could be polar opposites within himself. The active substance abuser may seem stricken with a vengeful or angry spirit, but it's really just his "addict-identity." It is this "addict-identity" that overpowers the person (host), becoming an obvious and tangible "monster." Families of those "inflicted" come to me to *exorcise* the "monster" that now inhabits their addicted loved ones. Little do they know that the "monster" or "demon" was there the whole time.

Humans are multidimensional creatures with many unknown capabilities, but with the unknown - comes unpredictable behaviors. If there is such a thing as "evil," I believe it is a part of all of us – a part of the human condition itself. We all have the potential for "good" and "evil," as "nature or nurture" factors tip our scales in one way or the other. Those with the disease of addiction somehow get their scales unfairly tipped in the wrong direction, and now their once hidden "addict-identity" fights with them in a duel to the death.

A Dual Duel to the Death

The dual nature of the entrenched addict keeps the "conflicting forces" at odds until death. Dual and duel are closely related words, with more in common than just their phonics. Dual usually refers to "two" like a "duo" or "pair," but duel refers to a contest between "two conflicting forces." In the duality of addiction, the contest involves two sides (a duo or pair) of the person. On the other hand, a duel is a fight for life, with the winner receiving dominion over the other half. So, helping someone beat her "addict-identity" before it wins the duel is a long process.

1. Recognizing and Understanding the Conflict

It doesn't matter if you're the addict's lover, counselor, or the addict itself; you will not conquer the addiction without first having a clear understanding of the conflict. A conflict is a dispute, disagreement, contention, or strife, usually between two parties. In this case, we have two distinct,

---

- ADDICT INSIGHT -

"AN ADDICT'S 'HOST' AND 'ADDICT-IDENTITY' NEVER FULLY SEPARATE. BOTH SIDES SHARE THE SAME MIND, BODY, BEHAVIORS, AND SUBSEQUENT CONSEQUENCES."

---

incompatible selves battling for supremacy. Therefore, addiction is inconsistent with a "normal" human lifestyle and vice versa. It is critical to recognize that this internal conflict starts as soon as the person begins "using and abusing" her DOC.

Knowing this helps you better understand that the "host" and the "addict-identity "are connected, but completely separate entities. As a result, the addiction is as much a part of an addict as her unique personality.

It is the addiction that makes addicts lie and manipulate. It is the addiction that also makes them engage in criminal acts. Thus, the "host" and the "addict-identity" are separate, but connected, which is why it is so hard to figure out an addict's true identity.

The key to understanding and overpowering this internal conflict is acknowledging and accepting that it exists. I'm not going to lie to you, recognizing this is often very hard for AAAs and their embarrassed families. Part of my years of intense battling with my addiction resulted from me trying to hide it and not acknowledge it. I was not proud of the diseased portion of me; however, I was still unwilling to admit it existed. Truthfully, I was like countless other "users and abusers," denying it, ignoring it, and fighting it without really fighting it.

Addicts swear up-and-down that, "It's not a part of who I really am..." or "It does not control me...." We deny its control over us or try to ignore its existence altogether. We act like it's not a part of us, not who we are – it's just how we operate. We deny that our druggy ways and associated behaviors come from us. Well, I'm here to tell you that if we exhibit those behaviors, it is a part of who we are.

I'm also here to tell both addicts and "helpers" that you don't have to love the "addict-identity," but you still need to be aware of its existence - for recovery to occur. The duality of addiction breeds contention between two opposing drives. It also triggers strife and ambivalence when seeking help for the disease.

Our ambivalence about its existence leads to resistance, and in turn, denial. What makes the duality of addiction worse is the denial that it even exists. That is why we have to address the addiction for the conflict to end. Without recognizing and understanding the war, the "addict-identity" will take the host out mortal combat style.

I talk about this duality to give you a better understanding of an addict's thoughts and behaviors. Understanding the internal conflict help addicts, "enablers," and their "helpers" defeat the addictive half. Understand that actions can be changed; however, the "addict part" of a person will always be there - that part is inseparable.

2. Divide and Conquer the "Addict-Identity"

It's not the drug's fault - it's the person's fault. The drug just activates another aspect of the person - one he already had – his "addict-identity." Many people question if it is "nature or nurture" that causes addiction. And, most mental health counselors and addiction experts will tell you it's 50/50. Half of the people who develop a SUD do so as a result of their environments, and half will say it's genetic - a predisposition to drugs or alcohol. Regardless of the cause, most addicts are born with "addict-identities" hidden deep inside of them. These identities arise when someone or something triggers it. You are just witnessing another part of them - another part of who they are.

In other words, an addict's "host" and his "addict-identity" never fully separate. Both sides share the same mind, body, behaviors, and subsequent consequences. Both are also distinct and separable, but only to a certain extent. Addiction is part of the addict's biopsychosocial makeup. This means that the disease is connected to him biologically through genetics, psychologically through reinforcement, and socially through social environments. These three elements are deeply ingrained in the addict, and each one **must** be treated together for a successful separation.

So, the goal is to divide the "addict-identity" from the person. Once the "addict-identity" has been successfully separated from the person, he can effectively move forward in recovery. How can you differentiate between the person and his "addict-identity?" By observing his actions and behaviors.

In other words, "Ye shall know them by their fruits!" Don't quote me on that, but I think it is in the Bible somewhere. I assume this verse means we will know a person by what they produce (her actions) like we know an apple tree because of the fruit it produces (Matt, 7:16, KJV).[8] The fruits of the "addict-identity" are, in no particular order, deception, thievery, disorderly conduct, cheating, depraved behaviors, criminality, and all-around dirty deeds.

It is imperative that all involved parties address these behaviors. Why? Because the "addict-identity" manifests itself in its actions, and it's those actions that you'll want to divide and conquer first before you address the more difficult task of working on the "host." In Chapter 6 of this book, I list three steps for addressing the behaviors of the "professional addict," aka someone, who has allowed his "addict-identify" to take control. Once you've singled-out the actions of the "addict-identity," the next step is to get the addict to address these problematic activities, especially those that encourage continued "use and abuse" patterns.

Keep in mind that the "host" of an "addict-identity" can address problematic behaviors through *self-evaluation*. But the addict must honestly ask herself if she genuinely wants to exhibit these behaviors. Honesty does not come easily to a person who is unaware that she is battling the "addict-identity" within. The truth is *self-reflection* is

---

8.   King James Version Bible. (n.d.) The Book of Matthew: 7:16.

more accessible during the latter "phases of addiction," after repeated stints in treatment or repeated negative consequences. At first, the "addict-identity" goes from being *just* a behavior to being a lifestyle choice, to being a state-of-being. Again, the "host" **must** be willing to ask an crucial question to herself. This question is, "Is this who I am and what I want to be?"

As an addiction counselor, I often tell my clients; if you don't want to be labeled an "addict," don't do what addicts do. I want the person suffering from a substance use disorder (SUD) to co-exist with his "addict-identity." He **must** be able to understand and control the destructive nature within. What does that mean? It means he **must** control his behaviors. My goal is to **stop** the "addict-identity's" progression, so it doesn't go from a secondary trait to a primary one. Because, if the "addict-identity" gets the opportunity to take control, it has gone way past *just* being a behavioral issue. Therefore, the key is to recognize, understand, and divide the "host" from his "addict-identity," so the person can regain control of himself.

The Question of "Who's in Control?"

I have chronicled the chronic struggle between two warring factions, a person vs. her "addict-identity." The duality of addiction is two separate but opposing "forces" within the same individual. *It's all about control.* No one *wants* to lose control of her own life. And, no one *wants* to be unable to master her own destiny. But the addict no longer has a *choice* in the matter. The tipping point in this internal conflict occurs when a person (knowingly or unknowingly) gives up control of herself to her "addict-identity," not giving a damn about anyone or anything. The person only cares about how and when she will receive the next "high." This often occurs during the end phase of addiction.

So, what you have here are two distinct versions of the same person co-existing in a combative nature. The two sides are not complementary; rather, they are opposing "forces." Someone or something has to be in control, right? Yes and no. The control shifts from the "host" to "addict-identity," and then back again, during this drawn-out conflict. Just like demon possession in the movies the "host" gets weaker the longer the conflict draws on. The parallels are undeniable.

Addiction is an involuntary possession by a "vile entity" called the "addict-identity." It is the "addict-identity" that assumes the role of a "puppet master" pulling the strings of the "host." The "host" is no longer in control once this "vile entity" hijacks his mind, body, and soul. In my case, I had no idea I was not in control. I was utterly seized, and my "addict-identity" limits no longer existed. At the time, I was capable of anything. Understand that *any* actively abusing person is capable of anything. Those closest to me saw the similarities between me and the fictional characters, Dr. Jekyll and Mr. Hyde, so much that they gave me that nickname. My sober self was introverted, respectful, and dependable, but my intoxicated self was a completely different story. This version of myself was loud, obnoxious, reckless, and dangerous. I was no longer in control, which meant I was capable of anything. The "addict-identity" fools its "host" into believing he is in charge and has free will in decision-making tasks when that couldn't be further from the truth.

The inability to control the "addict-identity" directly results from being unaware that there is a conflict brewing. As a result, the "host" unknowingly welcomes this "addictive demonic possession." It may even appear that the "host" enjoys giving his life over to self-serving carnal pleasures.

It's not like the "host" doesn't share in the "high," right? But, it's the insidious nature of this "possession" that fuels this pleasure-filled "high." The result? The "host" loses more of who he *used* to be. Then, the "host" becomes a hollowed-out shell of his former self, hardboiled eggshell thin. In other words, he becomes a full-blown addict. The addict may appear to *want* to be this way because fifteen-minutes of euphoria means more to him than family members, money, and anything else "normal" people hold dear. He may also appear to love the addiction because it is now a part of him, uncontrollable, but not intentional.

But an addict's liability is not dismissed simply because he cannot control his "addict-identity." **The addict must suffer the consequences of his actions if there is any hope of improvement and recovery.** However, if you're reading this book, you've probably already experienced the effects of addiction, as a loved one of an addict or as an addict yourself. Either way, relationships usually end badly, for addicts, during their active addictions. *As their tolerance for their drugs of choice increases, your tolerance for an addict's actions or lack thereof, decreases.*

So, if you are not already at the point where your tolerance level is redlining, you're on your way, believe me. Because addicts are internally conflicted, impulsive, manipulative, and ritualistic, relationships with them are usually unhealthy, dysfunctional, and risky. Now that you know and understand addiction's *real* definition and its dual nature, you can put them into context. In other words, they can help you better understand your relationship with an addict.

CHAPTER 3

The Relations of Addiction

Love cannot save you from your own fate.
— **Jim Morrison**
1943 - 1971
(Cause of Death: Exact Cause Unknown – Suspected Alcohol Poisoning)

An Addict's 'About Me'

If you had prior knowledge of the full extent of your spouse's or partner's addiction - would you *still* have pursued him?

Now, picture the online dating profile of an average substance abuser:

Name: John Hobo

Occupation: Unemployed, Semi-Functional Alcoholic

Location: In-Between Friends' Homes – Sleeping on their Couches

Favorite Quote: "Never Met a Drink I Didn't Like!"

About Me: Heavy Drinker with a Specialty in Making Embarrassing Scenes in Public. Unable to Form Solid Bonds with Other People. May Steal From Your Purse for Liquor Store Money. Prone to Alcohol-Fueled Violence

What I'm Looking For: Someone to Buy the First, Last, and All Rounds In-Between

Under "normal" circumstances - would this person be appealing to you? Hopefully not, but if this sounds like your current partner, you now know how "crazy" being in a relationship with him or her looks. Seriously. When I used - I lied, cheated, stole, made sacrifices for, gave all my time to, shunned friends, and even fought for my "liquid lover." But it was a very one-sided relationship. I invested a lot into it, but only received expensive chaos in-return. However, it was my family that suffered the most.

As a result, I've devised a plan of action for parents, relatives, and friends with loved ones who have a substance use disorder. Based on my experiences, as a "user and abuser," I would advise my ex-girlfriends to offer me something I can't readily get from alcohol and drugs.

If you are in a relationship with an addict, there are two things you can do to cope with it and keep from killing her before she achieves sobriety or abstinence.

Coping Methods for the Loved Ones of an Addict
❖ Substitute the Irreplaceable
What do you give the addict, who has everything wrapped-up in her addiction? To answer this question, you'll need to start with the obvious - the "high." The actual

"high" is what you're competing against, and it's a formidable foe because it's hardwired into the addict's brain.

More specifically, during drug use, neurotransmitters flood the brain, creating an association between the drug and the warm, fuzzy, ecstasy-like feeling it causes in the body. It is this feeling that is the basis for everything *wrong* in addiction. So, the answer to the question is... regardless of how difficult it is; you must find an alternative "high" for your addicted loved one. In other words, create new feelings of pleasure that have no association with "use and abuse."

Find out what mentally and physically turns your loved one on, before the drug use awakens her "addict-identity." Also, figure out what he enjoys, what she craves, and what he or she fantasizes about. Then, learn what calms her down and what gives her a sense of peace. Determine what your addicted love one liked to do before the drugs took it all away. Discover how she passed the time before she started getting "high." Many times, drugs are used as a way to combat boredom. After that, help your loved one find alternative forms of joy - ones that are unrelated to drugs or alcohol.

If your partner is an addict, do not underestimate the power of sex. Fight the biological with the biological. Addiction has a physical component and, so does sex. When a person has sex after drinking or drugging, neurotransmitters travel down the reward pathway, causing a pleasurable feeling in the body. Every addict's sexual preferences differ, so investigate the right "sexual enticer" for your situation. Sex is a powerful tool, so you need to know how to use it properly or even withhold it until you get the desired results. If you follow these suggestions, you'll have several tools in your "alternative 'high' toolbox."

But more important than having these tools is having a clear understanding of this disease and treating your partner with compassion and love. ***The truth is an addict resorts to drugs to fill a void, to secure an insecurity, or to numb some form of pain.*** So, offer your loved one an "alternative high." Before you do, you'll need to understand that, to an addict, the disease becomes her only comfort.

Ironically, the world doesn't label addicts as "sick," instead, they are labeled as "weak," "nasty," "depraved," and "immoral undesirables." Due to this inherent self-serving disease, addicts are hard even to like, nevertheless, love. In the perpetual dysfunction of my "use and abuse," what I needed most in a companion was understanding with a hefty dose of love and compassion.

❖ Give A Whole Lotta Love

It is imperative that a person in a relationship with an addict provides her with a compassionate love that contains patient endurance. During my alcohol-soaked drunken episodes, I "messed-up" more times than I can count, but what appeared to be a coherent decision to drink was anything but that. So, if you love a substance abuser, you must understand that her ability to stop drinking and drugging is impaired.

It is also imperative that you understand what may look like a lack of willpower is something more profound and sinister. ***Addiction appears to give you an amazing "high," but in reality, it's really just fool's gold.*** So, what you need to give your addicted love one is a substantial, real, and long-lasting love and understanding – exactly what she can't get from her drug of choice.

The funny thing is before I "got clean," I was extremely faithful to my "liquid lover." In other words, I was devoted to a lover who couldn't love me back and wasn't even alive. As a result, it broke my heart. There were several women I loved or at least I thought I loved, but my addiction made me hurt them.

In multiple relationships on multiple occasions, I had girlfriends call me, leaving anger-filled, anxiety-filled, fear-filled voicemails because they didn't hear from me for hours during my binges. For all they knew, I could've been dead in a ditch. They really loved me, but I needed them to love the addict part of me, as well - the part of me that was in constant conflict with my sober side.

But my exes and I didn't have the necessary resources to help me combat my disease and the "addict-identity" it produced. So, when deciding to continue any relationship with an addict, it is of utmost importance for you, the sober person, to be uncompromising when battling the addiction. In other words, you can't half-ass your attempts to help. ***Unyielding compassionate love from you could be the catalyst needed to help your loved one regain his power.***

So, by all means, offer *real* love to your addicted love one, because her DOC will not love her back. But, don't remove all limits from the love you give. By this, I mean, in loving a substance abuser, you can't give him unconditional love with no limits, because he will try to find a way to take advantage of it.

Period-point-blank, having unconditional love for someone with a substance abuse issue is the number one thing that will encourage him or her to continue "using and abusing."

Know Your Enemy

Like I stated in Chapter 1, addiction is a disease of the mind. It's not a *choice*. Rather, it's a slow form of suicide. Like what Sun Tzu said more than two-thousand years ago, "Knowing your enemy helps you win in a battle against it." Well, your addicted loved one, family member, partner, or friend is not the enemy; instead, it's the addiction that is the enemy, and it's a powerful one.

The sheer power of addiction is evident in the massive number of people who abuse, overdose (OD), live, and come back begging for more. You could compare it to many other things, but in my simple opinion, addiction's power is far greater than the power of love.

Speaking for myself, my love affair with my DOC was much more potent than any relationship I had ever been in – more than any woman I thought I loved. It was even stronger than the infatuation I felt for my first love. My addiction love was a love that made me smile from ear-to-ear and gave me butterflies in my stomach. Awake and with my eyes wide open it was a love that made me dream about it and anticipate our next encounter.

It's sad, but I was more dedicated to my relationship with alcohol than most couples are in their "committed" relationships. I passionately loved my "liquid lover," and the bottle it came in - its amber color and its enticing smell turned me on.

- ADDICT INSIGHT -

"THE ADDICT IN YOUR RELATIONSHIP CAN'T FULLY LOVE TWO LOVERS, HER DRUG LOVE 'OUT-LOVES' THE OTHER... MY 'LIQUID LOVER' HAD ME 'TILL DEATH DO US PART,' AND MY OTHER LOVES COULD NOT COMPETE."

Guess what was incredibly exciting? The sound of the bottle opening for the first time. It was almost like taking the panties off of a new hot lover.

I won't go into further details because I may get flashbacks, so I hope you get the picture with the addiction/love analogy. To sum it up, the bond and love I felt for the alcohol were tighter than a bully's headlock and the investment of time was longer than most marriages in this country. What I just described is the destruction, love, bond, investment, and power of addiction. Basically, the substance abuser gives unconditional love to something that doesn't love her back. My relationship with my drug of choice was one-sided, and those who were in relationships with me probably thought the same thing. So, if you're in a relationship with someone with a SUD, she isn't going to love you as she should, as long as she is "using and abusing." The truth is addicts can't fully love two lovers at the same time.

Part of me knew I couldn't and wouldn't put my all into a relationship - I was incapable of it. But I couldn't admit it to myself at the time. It seems like drugs and alcohol have a way of blocking the receptors in your brain - the ones that help you admit and accept stuff. Only now that I can admit something you must accept - your addicted love one can't fully love two lovers simultaneously. It's you or the DOC, and the DOC wins every time. I know I married my "liquid lover" 'till death do us part,' and my other loves could not compete.

Dysfunctional Functioning

By far, my longest committed relationship has been with alcohol. For eighteen-years, I courted, pursued, and with reckless abandon, loved my "liquid lover." I did occasionally cheat with other substances, but it always came back to it. Alcohol was my liquid lover, and my affection for it vomited on every aspect of my life. As our relationship progressed, all else became secondary. It didn't dawn on me that I was in deep until *I was in deep*. From lust to love to lovelorn, my "liquid lover" took me on an emotional roller-coaster ride - one I never wanted to get off.

The real-world definition of a dysfunctional addictive relationship is one in which one person is a ticking time bomb, and the other one is trying to hug him while trying to stay clear of the blast. It is a relationship where nothing is constant or sure, but drama and disappointment. With all this going on, it's no understatement that this type of connection is *doomed*.

Any relationship without loyalty is *doomed*. For instance, a dog is loyal to whoever has a treat. Well, an addict is loyal to whoever helps her obtain her drug of choice. In other words, she follows whoever is feeding her "addict-identity." How can you trust someone who may get "wasted" and forget all about you? How can you be committed to someone who may sell her body to get that next "high?" Well, a person with diminished inhibitions is capable of doing anything or having anything done to her to get what she wants.

If it's not already clear as day, then reading this chapter may help you gain a clearer perspective on being in a relationship with an addict. As the addiction progresses, anyone who cares about her will eventually develop ill feelings towards her. And, as time passes, feelings of disappointment will turn into animosity, and ultimately, hate.

I know you don't want things to progress to that point, so please continue to read. The two addiction coping methods I outlined in this chapter can help open up the way for lifesaving treatments. Keep in mind that a person's addiction to drugs and alcohol is the very definition of an abusive relationship.

I abused alcohol, and it abused me back.

Imagine being duped into falling for someone who made you feel so *right*, but turned out to be a "toxic monster." You wanted to run away from this "monster," but didn't because you were madly in love with it. Now, running away seems pointless. Just like a battered lover, I made excuses; I thought things would get better and that I could change the circumstances. Just like a battered lover, I was conflicted. Just like a battered lover, I was damn near beat to death before I finally took action.

As you read this, ask yourself, "How can I compete with my loved one's drug of choice?" Well, the answer is simple – you can't.

So, for the record, let's acknowledge that it is *impossible* to have a fruitful relationship with an AAA. Any type of connection is difficult, but relationships, in which trust is paramount, suffer the most. With addiction, the want, need, and cravings are all-encompassing.

For example, it's this physiological and the psychological thirst for "bad gas" that ruins the whole damn engine. The relationship your loved one has with her drug of choice is far more intimate and involved than the one she has with you. ***The sad fact is you, alone, cannot defeat the allure of your loved one's pills, powder, needle, or bottle.*** The sooner you accept this fact, the less you'll lose to addiction.

CHAPTER 4
The Cost of Addiction

I know I made a big mistake when I started using this shit...
My liver is not functioning. And, I'm throwing up all of the time and shitting my pants. The pain is more than I can handle. It's the worst pain in the world. "Dope sickness" hurts my entire body.
— **Layne Staley**, *Front Man for "Alice in Chains"*
1967 – 2002
(Cause of Death: *Heroin and Cocaine Intoxication*)

Addiction Debt

Looking back, it almost physically hurts to think about the costs associated with my addiction. Throughout the years, I accrued so much "addiction debt" that if there were addiction creditors, they would look at my bill, see I could never pay it off, and then give up trying to collect it. "Addiction debt" consists of what has been paid out, lost, and acquired due to direct or indirect substance abuse.

This debt is not just a burden for the debtor, but also those closest to him. Why? Well, these loved ones pay simply because they are associated with the addicts. Society, as a whole, bears some of the burdens, from paying higher taxes to paying higher insurance rates - all due to addiction-related issues. The truth is the abuse of tobacco, alcohol, and illicit drugs are costly to our nation, causing more than $740-billion annually in costs related to crime, loss of work productivity, and health care (NIDA, 2017).[9]

Therefore, in this chapter, I intend to explain "addiction debt" in-depth, so you can better understand the causes and effects of it. Then, I will give you tips on how you can prevent racking up so much "addiction debt."

Addiction Debt - Paid

What will the addiction of your spouse, family member, or friend cost you? Well, you can expect to pay out lots of money. You may think you know, but you have no idea. I'm going to keep it really real and break down some of the actual experiences other addicts, and I have had. Similar to the progressions found in the "phases of addiction," "addiction debt" is the progression of funds paid out during the course

---

9.   NIDA. (2017). Trends & statistics. Retrieved from https://www.drugabuse. gov/related-topics/trends-statistics

of the "use and abuse." The following scenarios are rough estimates, based on my AAA and counseling experiences.

At first, as a loved one, you pay for the alcohol and/or drugs in the most innocent situations (i.e., parties, concerts, birthday parties, social gatherings, special occasions, etc.). However, over time, the amount of money you spend on your loved one's "using and abusing" increases. In other words, the amount you spend on your loved one's "habit" progresses until you are spending approximately $25 to $355 weekly on drugs and alcohol.

Then, as the drug ingrains itself into your addicted loved one's life, the amount of money you shell out for drugs and alcohol (for her) increases even more. After a while, your addicted loved one starts to rely on you to pay for her drug/and alcohol "habit" *and* her bills. This can cost you between $100 and $200 a week.

At this point, your addicted love one has entered the "antisocial phase" of addiction. It is the "addict-identity's" desire for the drug and alcohol that is driving her actions and it is those actions that are leading to some pretty "messed-up" consequences. In other words, the drugs or alcohol fuels the fighting and stealing, which then leads to multiple arrests, and then having to come up with bail money ($200-$2000, per incident).

Addicts and families with money can pay for high-priced lawyers ($1000-$5000), but those without money

---

- ADDICT INSIGHT -

"BEING LOCKED UP IS A MULTIFACETED EXPERIENCE THAT'S HUMBLING, DEMEANING, SOBERING, AND EVEN ENLIGHTENING."

---

are forced to rely on uninterested public defenders. Additional funds are required when there are drug/alcohol-related criminal charges – i.e., multiple court appearances, fines, and court costs ($35 to $1500 per charge).

If the judge orders, probation fees can run between $50 and $100 per month. And, if the judge orders the addict to jail, there are additional costs, such as booking fees, canteen fees, phone fees, and even "residency fees" ($100 to $500 per month).

If the addict is charged with a DUI, DWI, or OWI, the costs can increase even more (about $10,000 per charge). Once released from jail or court, the addict no longer has a driver's license (it is suspended due to his drinking/drugging and driving), so he has to come up with gas money or some alternative form of transportation ($45 to $225 per week). To gain the license back, someone (you or the addict) **must** pay ignition interlock fees, driver assessment fees, license surcharges, and reinstatement fees ($75 to $500).

Oh, and don't forget the miscellaneous costs associated with alcohol and drug abuse, such as paying the dealer for the addict's debt ($100 to $600 monthly). Keep in mind that at this point, your addicted loved one has developed a physical dependency on her DOC and is now in the "advanced phase" of addiction. This means she has to "use" just to feel "normal." So, as you can see, it can get costly to prevent an addict from getting "drug sick" or selling herself on the corner for her DOC ($100 to $1000 per week).

Anymore costs? Yes! Once the addict enters treatment, there are SUD costs, such as intervention costs, rehab program costs, and drug/alcohol-related hospital costs ($100 to $20,000). Don't despair because addicts who can't afford treatment can have it paid through social service benefits, including Medicare/Medicaid.

My girlfriends, family members, and my "biker brothers" shared these costs with me. Like I mentioned above, if you are the loved one of an addict, you probably bought his alcohol or drugs – initially. However, once you witnessed the effects of the drugs or alcohol on your loved one, you probably started curbing how much you were spending on these vices for your loved one.

In my case, my "habit" only worsened with time, so instead of buying alcohol for me, my loved ones began paying for my grocery and gas bills. Why? Well, because my money was going to my "liquor lover." Plus, any cash they "loaned" me wouldn't be recouped, because I had become a "walking money pit." So, their "good intention funds" now went to paying my accident costs, hospital stay costs, DUI punitive costs, bail, court fines, and jail fees. Did you know that people have to *pay* to stay in jail nowadays? Well, it's true.

Paid in Full - Incarceration

I have taken many mug shots over the years and can honestly say I have a fascinating gallery of embarrassing pictures that show addiction's debilitating efffects. In these snapshots of my life, I go from intoxicatingly happy, to "fight night" bruised, to *Tasmanian devil* angry, to not-having-a-hope-in-the-world depressed.

Like many with my disease, my encounters with law enforcement and incarceration have been attributed to my "use and abuse." Although imprisonment appears to be a simple "do the crime - pay the time" kind of deal, it's so much more. The truth is being "locked up" is a multifaceted experience – one that is humbling, demeaning, sobering, and even enlightening. But, it's *still* a costly experience for the substance abuser and those who care about him.

Frankly, every time I went to jail - I paid a cost. In other words, I not only paid with money, but I also paid emotionally. However, my financial costs didn't remotely compare to the emotional toll I paid. I may have come across as a "tough guy," but I always had a truckload of heavy emotions swirling around inside of me. More specifically, simultaneously, I feared the "unknown," I had guilt for leaving my loved ones, I had stress because I wasn't earning money and I had anxiety that I might not make it out of there - alive. While I was in the "inside," those, who cared about me, experienced the same emotional toll, yet, I couldn't comprehend that until I became "clean."

So, even though most jails are bursting at the seams with inmates, it can *still* be a lonely place. Surrounded by unfamiliar faces, the faces I took for granted on the "outside," became sorely missed. The sterile coldness of correctional institutions can only be compared to the coldest and unwelcoming operating rooms (ORs). In my situation, this "coldness" was both figuratively and literally, because there were periods, while in jail, that I shivered like crazy. Maybe, it was due to the temperature in the jail or maybe, it was because of my frazzled nerves. Or, perhaps it was a combination of both temperature *and* nerves. I can't say for sure. But even more chilling was the overwhelming sense of finality when those metal doors clanked closed behind me.

Most addicts will eventually get "locked up," regardless of race, economic status, gender, or age. No amount of money will keep an addict entirely out of jail or prison. It's almost like a "rite of passage." As punishment, crime and incarceration are as much a part of addiction as drugs and alcohol. Only those with money or with families that have money get to spend less time behind bars.

I've been in the correctional system enough times to see that only the addicts, who *still* have people in their corners, are overjoyed when they hear their names announced for release. The more times I went to jail, the fewer times people helped me get released. But jail can cause you to become impatient. It can make you *feel* like life on the "outside" is moving on without you, while you are "stuck" on "snail mode" in the "inside." But, after a while, I just became accustomed to the idea that no one was going to come for me. In other words, I knew I wasn't going anywhere anytime soon.

Addiction Debt - Lost

What will the addiction of your loved one cause you to lose? The truth is an addict can lose everything - down to his very life. The thing is most addicts have no problem taking you (loved ones) with them. "I've lost so much from this addiction" is the biggest understatement of my entire life. I thought to help other addicts "get clean" was frustrating, but it's ten times worse when you're the addict losing at every turn in life. As an addict and "enabler," I have gained experience on *both* sides of the addiction battle. And guess what? *Both* sides are draining.

Losing Everything

For me, the worst part of addiction was having no control over the things I was losing. It felt like I was just giving my prized possessions away for free at a yard sale. I got so used to losing my belongings that I didn't even replace them. What was the point? Thus, the internal conflict for addicts lies in their desire to keep the "things" they worked so hard to obtain, while, at the same time, only having a real desire for the very substance that caused them to lose what they worked so hard to get. I used to dwell on the material things I lost, but in hindsight, it's the non-material things I regret losing the most.

What have I lost?

I lost love - I've been blessed to have had many great women in my life. But, those who told me they loved me and proved it through their actions were often "gifted" stress from my addiction, in return. The truth is my "liquid lover" ended most of my romantic relationships. It caused me to push potential lifelong partners away, alienating them so that they wouldn't love me.

I lost people - My "liquid lover" ended most of my other relationships, as well. The effort I put into drinking

---

- ADDICT INSIGHT -

"WE, ADDICTS, CONSTANTLY TALK ABOUT PEOPLE, PLACES, AND THINGS THAT COULD BE TRIGGERING. HOWEVER, IT'S THOSE SAME PEOPLE, PLACES, AND THINGS THAT WE 'MESS UP' AND THEN SCRAMBLE TO GET BACK!"

---

helped me neglect others and dismiss the value of having genuine human interactions. Honestly, I liked alcohol better than I liked people. Why? Because it provided me with a level of comfort, I could not find in others. But as my drinking got worse - my antisocial behaviors increased.

So, what did I do?

I distanced myself from people, and they distanced themselves from me.

I lost my reputation – Before the addiction, my family, friends, and coworkers saw potential in me, based on my actions, grades, and work. But, during the addiction, all they saw was my "addict-identity." Then, I became known *only* for my addiction.

So, I went from having "promise" to breaking promises to becoming Mr. "He could've been..." or "He should've been... but now he's *just* a 'drunk.'"

I lost my freedom – Every time I was jailed, I gave up my freedom. The correction officers told me when to eat, sleep, and shit.

The powerlessness of being an inmate is beyond anything I had ever experienced up until that point. Yet, I didn't appreciate this loss of freedom until I threw it away. Being "locked up" was a loss of the most basic of privileges we often take for granted.

I lost time - My addiction took damn near *everything* from me. Fortunately, material things can be replaced, and relationships healed. However, precious time can never be recouped. As a result, I wasted hundreds of hours drinking and even more trying to recover from hangovers. It was time lost - time that could have been used to do something productive with my life. But, instead, my "habit" began to steal my life.

More specifically, my "use and abuse" stripped me of any positive steps I took to regain control of my life. When I tried to move forward, my "habit" pushed me back at least two steps. I tried to invest time into developing healthy relationships with good people, especially good women, *only* to torch the very bridges they were standing on. I spent money and valuable time relocating to new places to start anew *only* to make the same mistakes again in the new location.

I snagged my dream jobs only to lose them because I could not handle the workload due to being hungover and making stupid decisions. We addicts continuously talk about people, places, and things that could be triggering. However, it's those same people, places, and things that we "mess-up" and then scramble to get back. So, the sooner we *all* learn lost time can **never** be recouped, the better.

A Lost "Enabler"

I used to be clueless about addiction and how to help others with this disease. So, I wrote this book for those unknowing "enablers," who have been taken advantage of... like I once was. The truth is until you come to some realizations, you will continue to lose just as much as your addict-ed love one.

I lost addicts – Addiction robbed me of people I loved and once trusted. Addicts, I would give *almost* any-thing, stole from me to get their "highs." It wasn't so much about the "things" I lost, but more about being looked in the eyes and deliberately lied to. There is jolting disbelief when the person you love is unrecognizable to you due to his "habit." For me, it was even harder to deal with the fact that people *chose* drugs over me.

I lost peace - The addicts I was trying to help add-ed another level of stress and worry to my life – one that I wasn't fully equipped to handle. I had little "peace of mind" during this time because my thoughts were constantly run-ning laps in my mind, thereby keeping me up at night. "Are they ok?" "Where are they right now?" "What are they do-ing right now?" "Are they coming home tonight?" "Are they going to take advantage of me or someone else?" "Are they 'locked up?' " "Are they going to overdose?" "Are they going to die?"

Anxiety is a common side-effect of being an "enabler."

I lost patience - You have to pay more attention to an addict than you do a toddler. I have close family mem-bers who are suffering from dual diagnoses - addiction and mental health issues. So, believe me when I tell you that some addicts have a way of burning my patience faster than cheap gas in a V8 engine. My sister does things because of her "crack habit" that makes me want to take a crowbar to her head. Time and time again, she would look at me in my eyes while lying to me about minor stupid things. When she does this, I know good-and-well she is lying, but she just keeps on lying to me - and I keep losing my patience.

I almost lost my mind - Trying to "clean up" after others' drug-fueled mistakes nearly drove me crazy. My addicted family members had me search for them after disappearing to find their DOCs. This took time. I also had to bail them out of jail over and over again. That also took time. If I couldn't pay their bails, I had to visit them in jail, giving away even more time. Moreover, I had to try and talk them down whenever they called, saying, "I don't want to be here anymore." Lots of time spent. The truth is caring for those who don't care about themselves is the ***worst*** kind of mental angst.

I lost sleep - If I could... all I would do all day is ride my motorcycle, have lots of fantastic sex, eat delicious food, and gets tons of sleep. If I ever win the lottery, I plan to make sleep my full-time job - that's how much I love sleeping. Anytime my sleep is interrupted because the addict living with me was in-and-out of the house all night, I get mad as hell.

Addiction Debt - Acquired

Debt is about more than just what you pay or lose. Addiction "gifts" a lot of unwelcomed debt to all parties involved. Being on both the "user" and "enabler" sides of the equation, I've had to deal with each of its repercussions for a while.

I acquired illnesses - My addiction made me sick. Unsuccessfully dealing with others' addictions also made me sick. The toll it had on my mind and body was real. My pattern was depression, then self-medication, and then back to depression, a never-ending cycle with periods of vomiting until I had no stomach acids left to throw up. Truth-be-told, I was on my way to cirrhosis of the liver, but I ended up with incontinence from years of "breaking the seal" instead. Now, I have to take my meds and get to a bathroom in time not to "leak." But I know it could be worse. Some addicts develop "meth mouth," scaly, scarred skin, yellow eyes, and acquired infections from weakened immune systems. I thank God I didn't catch an STD from all of the women I had unprotected sex with during my binges. But, even if you're not the addict, you probably *still* have anxiety from caring for one.

I acquired scars - During my professional drinking career, I've received physical and mental wounds that may never heal. I don't remember a lot about the fights I've fought, but my body bears the scars from them. Scars I probably wouldn't have if it weren't for my "use and abuse." I *still* have dreams of being "locked up" again for my actions and PTSD flashbacks similar to an old war vet's. Guilt is also a recurring scar that *still* haunts my sober self.

I acquired bills – "Financial ruin" is the best phrase to describe addiction's long-term impact on your money. What the "addict" or "enabler" doesn't pay for at the time will eventually pop-up in the form of bills, fines, surcharges, liens, etc. When I started paying to clean-up one "mess," I would drink my way into another one, increasing my debt until I was drowning in it. It felt like I was trying to swallow the water I was drowning in to save myself.

I acquired terrible experiences - From getting jumped by eight guys in a bar, unable to fight back because I was too "wasted" to beating a guy bloody until he hit the ground, lifeless because he touched my truck - there were a lot of traumatic experiences I got and gave. As addicts, we tend to remember the "bad things" more than the "good things." And, when it comes to addiction, things are mostly bad. I used to feel good - I even had some good times; however, it was just my way of forgetting the bad times – i.e., the embarrassment and guilt.

Addiction Debt Death

The most significant cost of addiction is the loss of life. "Addiction debt" takes its most impactful toll in the eventual deaths of those addicted.

It is a slow form of suicide that does not stop until it rips every ounce of humanity and life from the addict and those closest to him.

We all know that mortality is a fact of life. We all live and die. The problem with addiction-related deaths is that a large part of the population *still* has an "oh well" attitude about it. In other words, many believe the "addiction myths" and feel like it was the addict's lack of willpower that finally led to his demise.

The family, friends, and loved ones of those, who have suffered losses due to substance use disorders, are usually the *only* ones advocating for change. If you analyze the media, pop culture, and various political stances, it'll feel like

---

- ADDICT INSIGHT -

"WE ARE NOT 'BAD' OR 'EXPENDABLE UNDESIRABLES' BECAUSE WE ABUSE SUBSTANCES; RATHER, WE ABUSE SUBSTANCES BECAUSE, FOR SOME REASON, WE FEEL LIKE 'BAD' OR 'EXPENDABLE UNDESIRABLES.'"

SUD related deaths, connected illnesses, and overdoses are accepted outcomes. Well, that's bullshit!

Treating addiction-debt-death as if it is commonplace in our society is unacceptable. Addicts' lives are worth just as much as anyone else's. We are not "bad" and "expendable" undesirables, because we abuse substances; rather, we abuse substances because, for some reason, we *feel* like "bad" and "expendable" undesirables. Keep in mind that just like there are homeless "penniless addicts," there are also fancy "millionaire addicts." Thus, part of my job is to teach the public that there is no difference between them.

Even with all the money, power, respect, and supporters in the world, there have been many well-off people who lost their battles to "addiction debt." Being born with a silver spoon in your mouth or talent to make others stand in awe doesn't prevent you from becoming an addict. There have been rich and famous addicts that have died alone, just like unknown, poor addicts.

And guess what? Many of these people are my heroes. I have included quotes from many of them at the beginning of the chapters. Some of the celebrities you may know or have heard of. Regardless, they influenced me because I listened to them. It's crazy how people you've never met can have such a massive impact on your life and how their deaths can resonate with you long after they have passed away.

Addiction killed all of my heroes.

None of them should've died the way they did. Their deaths, like most drug/alcohol-related deaths, could have been prevented. All of my 90's-era rock heroes died prematurely – i.e., Kurt Cobain of *Nirvana*, Scott Weiland of *Stone Temple Pilots*, Lane Staley of *Alice on Chains*, Shannon Hoon of *Blind Melon*, and Chris Cornell of *Soundgarden*. Michael Jackson, Prince, and Whitney Houston also made great music, and they too died prematurely from drugs and alcohol.

I wish I *could* have been there for Kurt Cobain... If I had known him, I *wouldn't* have let him out of my sight until I was confident he was receiving the proper treatment for this disease. Maybe, I *would* have paid a security guard to monitor him. Possibly, I *would* have confiscated all of his guns. Perhaps, I *would* have given him ultimatums to get him to comply. Maybe, I *would've done a lot of things to save him....*

As each year passes, since Kurt's death, fans of good music try to fill the void he left. So much should have been done, and so much could have been done for him. Understand that I'm not referring to giving him special treatment because he was a celebrity. I'm referring to basic empathic substance abuse treatments. If only we would or could treat every addict like this. I believe we can, and we **must**.

So, instead of "I should've" or "I could've," turn it into "I did." Do all you can within your power to help, so no one complains that you stood by and didn't do anything. Follow your addicted loved one to rehab, detox, treatment, etc. Guard the exits so she can't leave.

Get your addicted loved one an electronic monitor; track her phone calls, etc. If your loved one is past the point of caring about her life, and she is a danger to herself and others, intervene, and ask the court for help. **But do something**! You wouldn't sit idly by and watch someone slit her wrists or douse herself with gasoline, would you? No. Well, addiction is just another form of suicide.

"Addiction-debt-death" is a projected outcome, but it should **never** be an accepted outcome.

Drug/alcohol-related deaths are preventable. Thus, the key to lowering one's risk of developing this disease and preventing it from progressing is being educated on the disorder – i.e., its definition, causes, signs, effects, and treatments. To better understand this disease - prevention, empathy, and education are crucial.

How to *Not* Pay, Lose, or Acquire So Much Addiction Debt

1. Say "No"

Keep in mind that an addict may steal from you from time-to-time, but ultimately you and only you have control over what you spend. Just like no one puts a gun to an addict's head to force him to abuse substances, no one puts

---

- ADDICT INSIGHT -

"JUST LIKE NO ONE PUTS A GUN TO OUR HEADS TO ABUSE SUBSTANCES, NO ONE PUTS A GUN TO YOURS TO SPEND MONEY TO 'ENABLE' US."

---

a gun to yours to spend money on an addict's "habit." The only difference between the two situations is that addicts have a *real* biological excuse. You must be knowledgeable of what is most likely going to happen if you continue spending money on your addicted loved one's "habit." Just from reading this book, you now have a real-world definition of addiction and its phases. If your loved one's actions fall under the definition of addiction, or if she has officially been diagnosed with a substance use disorder, then do not pay for drugs or alcohol under any circumstances.

2. **How to say "No"**

There is a very thin line between "helping" and "enabling" an addict, which I will detail in a later chapter. However, once you fully understand how this disease leads to death and losses, it will be easier to say, "No!"

❖ **Say "No" Quick:** Give a quick response, which cuts out any BS.

❖ **Say "No" Often:** Addicts are some of the most persistent people on the planet, so they will continue to ask you for what they want. So, keep saying, No!" In other words, say, "No!" to any use-related requests – i.e., paying-off a dealer, paying for street pills to avoid withdrawal symptoms, etc. You may think its harsh, but it's for the addict's own good.

❖ **Say "No" for Your Loved One's Sake**: Your mindset should be that of a responsible adult caring for an irresponsible child. An addict cannot make the *right* choices, because of his SUDs. So, you can't put money in an addict's hands or pay for his "habit." If the word "No" is too hard for you to say, then use "can't" because that implies it's out of your control. Remind your addicted love one that this is for his own good, and one day when his brain is not clouded, he will understand.

3.   Don't Take It Personal

Mark my words, as your "addict insider," ***we will selfishly waste your time as if your sole purpose is to fulfill our cravings.*** We will also repeatedly destroy your trust in us like a toddler who deliberately knocks over a "house of cards." The truth is we will bring recurring chaos to your peaceful existence just when you think all is well. It's not personal - it's in an addict's nature to take advantage of those closest to her.

It is important to understand that firmly saying "No" to an addict is saying "Yes" to being called every hurtful name in the book. It's saying "Yes" to feeling guilty because you feel obligated to help. It is also saying "Yes" to worry because you don't know what she will do now that you have closed the door on her personal "drug fund piggy bank."

It doesn't matter if the addict is your teen, spouse, or lifelong friend, you *will* get the brunt of her animosity, but don't take it personally. Developing cowhide-leather-thick-skin will help you keep control. Just let the substance abuser rants go in one ear and out the other, while *still* saying "No." Don't give in. The hardest thing to do is to do nothing, but doing nothing may save both of you a lot of heartache in the long run.

4. Drain You

There is a direct correlation (link) between addiction progression (in a loved one), the losses and collateral damage you experience because you care. Your finances and patience will be drained faster than a smartphone battery. The money and material things you lost when trying to help your addicted loved one can be replaced, but what you can't get back is far more valuable - your time, trust, and peace.

And, although it may not seem like it at the time, this is a life-or-death situation - with death being one-more-hit, "high," and/or drink away. You see, what starts as you paying for the bar tab can ends in you paying for a funeral. Do not contribute to this disease in any way.

So how much is enough "addiction debt?" Only you can answer that. The total of what you will pay, the things you will lose, and the debt you will acquire will largely depend on the amount of aid you feel comfortable rendering. Again, as your "addict insider," my advice is to say "No" to all requests for money, once you realize your loved one has a problem with drugs or alcohol. You want to help your loved one – I get it. However, enabling her "habit" may lead to her death. Are you prepared for that?

CHAPTER 5

To Enable is to Kill

*I don't need help because if I can't help myself, I
can't be helped.*
— Amy Whinehouse
1983 - 2011
(Cause of Death: Alcohol Poisoning)

Can I Help You?

As I have stated before, **being addicted to drugs is
like a slow form of suicide**. Each hit, shot, "high," and
drink edges the body closer off the cliff a closer to certain
death. If it's not the drug, then it's our actions that do us in.
Addicts would happily pay to kill themselves, drunk march-
ing like cows to the slaughterhouse. We are not alone on our
path towards *self-destruction*. **Forget the dealer, doctor, bartender, or "bookie," it's our own families,
unwittingly paving our ways into addiction-related oblivions**.

Consider the following questions:

1. Have you tried to protect the addict in your life from
going into withdrawal?

2. Have you ever bailed your addicted loved one, in jail on drug-related charges, out of jail? If so, why?

3. Have you ever lied or covered for the AAA in your life?

4. Do you keep giving the AAA in your life chances to change?

5. Have you ever paid for drugs and/or alcohol to keep the AAA from going out to get them?

6. Have you ever paid the addict's utility or phone bill to retain the services on for him?

7. Do you have a habit of cleaning up after the addict's drug-fueled mistakes and "messes?"

8. Have you ever paid the addict's dealer or bartender for an unpaid debt?

If you answered "Yes" to any of these questions, you have unwittingly played the role of "enabler." Webster's Dictionary defines an "enabler" as one who "enables" another to achieve an end and one who enables another to continue self-destructive behaviors (i.e., substance abuse) by pro-

---

- ADDICT INSIGHT -

"THIS IS THE FALLACY OF ADDICTION ENABLING - OUR ADDICTION TRAPS US, THEN WE NEED HELP GETTING OUT OF THE TRAP, BUT THAT HELP ONLY GETS US STUCK FURTHER IN THE TRAP."

viding excuses for or making it possible to avoid the consequences of such behaviors (Merriam-Webster.com,2020).[10]

When an addict is low on money, he will ask his family for more. When an alcoholic husband gets "locked up" for being reckless, he will call his wife to get him out. When the heroin user is on the verge of "dope sickness," she will call her friend to help her "score," providing a detailed account of the excruciating pain she'll be in if she doesn't get her "fix." As a result, her friend will feel guilty and comply. ***Assisting is not always the same as helping because if you are helping someone, you aren't necessarily doing a good deed.***

Being an "enabler" is the worst thing you can do for an addict. "Enablers" have a misguided idea that they're helping the addict by taking care of any issues. But, "enablers" are actually hurting addicts because they are helping to continue the addictive behaviors. They might as well stick a needle in the arm of a heroin addict or pour whiskey down the throat of an alcoholic!

By "helping" an addict avoid the negative consequences of his abuse, you are effectively helping him right into an early grave. Based on my struggles, and the knowledge I've gained working as a professional in this field, most people

---

10. Merriam-Webster.com. (2020). Enabler. Retrieved from https: www.merriam-webster.com/dictionary/enabler

with SUDs *only* change when forced to confront the negative consequences of their actions.

Helping or Hindering?

As you assist a drug user, in many instances, you are unintentionally continuing the cycle of drug abuse. To help is to hinder. This is the fallacy of "addiction enabling" - their addiction traps them, then they need help getting out the trap, but that help only gets them "stuck" even further in the trap. Remember, addicts are master manipulators. They depend on your kind-hearted donations for their next "euphoric high."

The truth is I enabled my AAA sister for years. When I became sober, I felt like it was my responsibility to help her get and remain drug-free, simply because she is related to me. I hated everything crack did to her and what she did for crack. I blamed the rock and not her when she stole my wallet while I was asleep or pawned my stuff while I was at work.

On several occasions I had to confiscate her debit card (she had her social security check deposited into it every month). I put quite a bit of effort into budgeting her money and paying her bills, even though she was older than me and with fewer responsibilities at the time. I gave my sister a small amount of money to buy food and tampons each month. But, when she started acting "crack-paranoid" again, it became apparent that she was *still* getting "high." I found out that my sister was taking the money I gave her for "personal items" buying crack. Yet, she *still* managed to "rack up" a large amount of debt from her dealer.

I honestly believed she would "get clean" based on my efforts, but that did not happen. All that time and effort I put into taking care of my sister's finances only provided her with fewer responsibilities and more time to get "high." My want or need to protect her because she was female, and a member of my family, hindered her growth and recovery. So, it is vital to recognize the difference between helping and hindering someone with a substance use disorder. How is one to tell the difference between real helping or "enabling" a substance-abusing loved one? All things considered, "helping" includes giving help to him or her, which is straightforwardly identified with recuperation and collectedness. "Enabling" is "helping" your dependent AAA maintain a strategic distance from responsibility, prolonging his or her cycle of dependence.

The following are examples of "enabling" and "helping." Review each event and its set of circumstances, then decide if it's either "enabling" or "helping."

1. Your 20-year-old son is home from college for the summer. During his stay, you notice his appearance is disheveled, and he seems "hungover" most the time. Also,

his room smells of vomit. He is also easily irritated by your questions.

Then, one night he goes out drinking with his friends. After getting into a street fight, he's charged with aggravated assault, resisting arrest, and disorderly conduct. He is placed in jail, given bail, and assigned a court date for the next week. He calls you collect and tells you what happened. You bail him out immediately.

Are you "enabling" or "helping" him?

Now, your son could be going through several issues that could be triggering his drinking behaviors. He could be experiencing a breakup with his college girlfriend or just starting the early stages of alcohol addiction. We know from the situation is that your son displays the criteria for a SUD, and his alcohol-fueled behavior has led to severe criminal charges.

But your son is young and still capable of learning to refrain from alcoholic antisocial behaviors. There is no better learning tool than incarceration. Since he has a court date a week from the day he was jailed, it wouldn't hurt to let his ass sit there and think about his actions. Bailing him out too soon is "enabling."

2. Or, let's say, your father calls you for help after spending his monthly disability check on alcohol and "street painkillers." This month he asks you for cash to pay his income-based rent and reduced electricity bill. You think

about it and then decide not to give him the money. Instead, you offer to pay his bills because he's getting older, and you feel obligated to care for him.

Are you "enabling" or "helping" him?

Based on the information we have, we know your father has a recurring problem with drugs. As a result of this problem, he doesn't have enough money to pay his bills. The thing is your father has the same "habit" of using - going broke - asking for help – and repeating the cycle. It's almost as if he *expects* you to help him with his bills. But, paying your father's bills out of obligation, guilt, or just to shut him up, is not addressing the problem – his drug abuse. Paying his bills keeps him from suffering the consequences of his actions, so it's "enabling."

3. What about this scenario? Your crack-smoking sister has accrued a massive debt from her dealer. The dealer gets your number from her and states if she doesn't pay what's owed, he will have to "teach her a lesson." Out of fear, you give her the money to pay off her debt.

Are you "enabling" or "helping" her?

Keep in mind that this situation could turn into a dangerous problem for you and her. Assuming this dealer is like most dealers, who will do almost anything to get their money, there is a good chance he means what he says.

The threat of violence could be *real*, or the person could just be posing, as a dealer, when he is actually only one of

> # - ADDICT INSIGHT -
> ## "ULTIMATELY THE ADDICT'S LIFE AND SOBRIETY ARE HIS OWN RESPONSIBILITY."

your sister's "get high buddies," who is looking to take advantage of you.

This situation is territory for law enforcement. It is essential to understand that giving money to a drug dealer is not solving the addiction issue; instead, it is "enabling" it.

4. Here is another one - A close friend of yours has just overdosed on a combination of heroin and fentanyl. You were the one who brought him back by administering Narcan to him. He's overdosed in the past but told you not to call 911 if it ever happened again because his opioid use would be recorded, and he'd be sent back to jail for violating probation. You decide not to call emergency services.

Are you "enabling" or "helping" him?

Well, even after being revived, he *still* doesn't look well, but you don't call 911, as he requested. Your friend just got as close to death as an addict can without dying. You helped save his life, but at the same time, you left the door open for him to go through another overdose.

In other words, by not calling 911, you kept a sick person away from qualified professionals. By not calling 911, you continue to play an edge of death game, similar to the movie *Flatliners,* in which med students play with death by stopping their hearts and then resuscitating each other. So, by not calling for help, you provided no real benefit to your friend. However, the one thing you did do is "enable" his drug use.

How *Not* to "Enable" an Addict

I came up with a simple acronym to cover the major steps of stopping "enabling" behaviors.

A.R.M. = Accept, Redirect, and Motivate

Accept: Accept that your loved one's addictive acts are outside of your control and not your responsibility. This may seem cold-hearted, and you may feel guilty or in fear of what could happen to your addicted loved one; however, it's the best thing you can do for him.

Also, accept that love and family ties are not binding contracts, so you are not obligated to help someone who doesn't want your help. It's heartbreaking to see the ones you love suffer – I get it. Every part of you wants to help her in any way you can. But you **must** accept that you, alone, cannot "cure" her disease. Your loved one is *broken* in a way that you can't "fix."

The truth is accepting things that are beyond your control takes lots of practice and a strong resolve. This is accomplished by having a strong mind and not a weak heart. I know it's easier said than done, especially for the mother, who can't bear the thought of her 1st born child being homeless and out in the cold, or a friend, who can't stand idly by, while her grade school buddy panhandles on the street. A weak heart asks the mind, "If I don't help her, who will? This is the last time!" The weak mind sounds just like a played-out love song.

Your instincts tell you to help the addict in her time of need. But, before you jump into action, train yourself to take a step back so that you can re-evaluate the situation. Ask yourself if what you're about to do will help your addicted loved one achieve sobriety or be a temporary "fix" until cravings for the next "high" roll around. There's a very thin line between "helping" and "hindering," but a logical mind is better at recognizing which is which, compared to an emotional mind. Having a firm resolve can help you put logic over emotion. Logic tells us that ***ultimately the addict's life and sobriety are his responsibility.*** "Enablers" **must** accept this logic if they are going to help their addicted loved ones recover.

Redirect: Redirect responsibility away from yourself and back towards the addict. I said it before, and I'll repeat it - **addicts are master manipulators.** They will make you feel guilty and blame you like you are the one who is doing the drugs. Addiction and irresponsibility go hand-in-hand like bikers and leather. Your addicted loved one's actions will make you feel like it's your duty to take care of what she can't or refuses to do. It is **not** your responsibility to take on the duties of an adult addict.

Do not be soft during this step. But be prepared. Be prepared for what, you ask? Well, when you redirect responsibility back to the addict, he or she will give you all types of interference, from being emotionally-abusive or verbally-abusive to being defiant or threatening. Develop a strong mind and cast aside a weak heart to deflect any crap they attempt to throw at you.

Redirect your addicted loved one's aggression and frustration back at him while reminding him how his "messed-up" actions have ended. Remind your addicted loved one that it's **not** your responsibility to do what he should be doing for himself. Redirection could cause the AAA to spiral downward, but this could also be the time for motivation.

Motivate: Motivate the addict to seek a moment of clarity. Honestly, the *only* thing that finally motivated me to get sober was the weight of the negative drunk shit I had committed. I felt like I was drowning in the air the last time I was in jail. The negative consequences felt like I was pushing a broken-down Harley up a Georgia hill in the August heat. In other words, my body was beaten, my strength was gone, and I was too exhausted. It was then that I made a promise to God and myself *never* to "use" again. And, I've been clean ever since. That was my moment of clarity – the beginning of my growth.

> # - ADDICT INSIGHT -
> ## "YOU MUST ALLOW AN ADDICT TO HAVE HER MOMENT IN THE NEGATIVE TO MAKE HER WANT THE POSITIVE."

Therefore, an addict must experience the consequences of his or her actions. I'm a firm believer that adversity breeds positive changes in most people, and those with SUDs are no exception. But, when you "enable" the addict, you take away her experience of negative consequences. So, allow the addict to have her moment in the negative to make her want the positive.

To motivate an addict to "get clean," you have to allow the negative to happen, which means you may have to do nothing when it does happen. While the addict is experiencing these consequences, remind her how she got to that point in the first place. Stay strong and *only* offer your help if she agrees to accept professional treatment or show a positive change in their actions.

Simple words of motivation can go a long way. "You can do it!" "You can do it for yourself!" "Keep trying!" and "Keep fighting!" all are phrases addicts don't hear enough from the people who love them. Motivate your addicted loved one with more kind words and fewer "enabling" actions.

Fig. 5-1

Simple But Difficult = Difficultly Simple

The most difficult relationship to maintain is one with a substance abuser. You feel sorry for him and want to help him "get clean," so he can be a productive member of society – I get it. You feel obligated to care for your addicted loved one like he is your responsibility. I get that too. So, you try your best to help him, even though he continually lies to you. You give and give until you can't give anymore, but your loved one's problems keep getting worse and worse. Your intentions are right - it's your execution that sucks.

How do you know if you're "helping" or "enabling" the addict in your life? Well, "helping" involves assisting her – aid directly related to recovery and sobriety. "Enabling," on the other hand, is "helping" your addicted loved one avoid accountability, thus, continuing her cycle of addiction. I don't know if it was just me or just my "messed-up" way of thinking, but it seemed like I attracted "enablers."

I blame no one but myself for my alcoholic actions, but I had more "enablers" than there are big belly bearded men in motorcycle clubs. The people around me never seemed to fully understand the depths of my addiction, even with all the trouble I caused them. Looking back now, it would have been better for me if my "enablers" had refused to help me.

The hardest thing to do is to do nothing when trying to save the addict in your life. "Enabling" comes naturally to those who care about people with SUDs.

By "enabling" an addict, you are only helping the addiction continue. However, by doing nothing, you are actually encouraging your addicted loved one to seek treatment. Using the A.R.M approach, you are using different execution methods to provide *real* help to her.

What you are attempting to do is save your addicted loved one's life in the long run. But, understand that by not "enabling" your addicted loved one, she will temporarily face some hard times and inconveniences. This is good for her. But you will *still* get some "clap back" (opposition), so you must develop a very thick skin.

Addiction develops resilience, so you will need to develop yours, as well.

The underlying key here is to refuse to do what the addict is capable of doing for herself. I was "enabled" for years, suffering, before I got my moment of clarity. I also "enabled" for years before I could face reality. My want and will to "help" my sister "get clean" was useless, because, at the time, she didn't want to "get clean."

The truth is we all have problems, so I had to address mine and let her hurt until she got tired of hurting. It's sad but true. So, you **must** stop "enabling" your addicted loved one. Why? Well, because to "enable" her is to kill her. Keep in mind that before an addict reaches her final destination, she often becomes a "professional addict."

CHAPTER 6

The Professional Addict

I can tell you that I'm not self-destructive. I'm not a person, who wants to die. I'm a person, who has life and wants to live.

— *Whitney Houston*

1963 - 2012

(Cause of Death: Drowning - Cocaine and Prescription Drug Intoxication)

Who is a "Professional Addict?"

What do you get when you add the following characteristics?

- ✓ impulsive, manipulative, and ritualistic substance abuser
- ✓ tons of addiction debt
- ✓ <u>+ years of "being enabled"</u>

Answer = a "professional addict"

A "professional addict" status involves a combination of lived experiences and alcohol or drug "use and abuse" experiences.

It represents an addict moving from the "Advanced Phase" to the "End Phase" of addiction. In Chapter 1, I explained my version of the "Phases of Addiction." Remember, the "Experimental Phase?" Well, it is just that – a "potential addict" "experiments" with drugs and alcohol because of curiosity or peer pressure.

Next is the "Social Phase," where the "potential addict" increases her use of drugs and alcohol during social occasions (i.e., parties, social gatherings, etc.) to experience euphoria and pleasure. However, this type of "use" can lead to "abuse."

After that comes the "Antisocial Phase." This phase occurs once the addiction has set-in. During this time, the "addict-identity" internally overpowers the person, dictating any external behaviors. This is where the more serious "use and abuse" consequences occur.

Then, there is the "Advanced Phase." This phase is marked by acknowledging the problem, the desire to end the problem, and any negative consequences associated with the problem.

The "End Phase" is the final stage. During this phase, control and hope are lost. This is when a serious intervention is needed to preserve the addict's life.

Once the addict seeks treatment for his "habit," he enters the "Remission Phase." This phase is marked by a period of abstinence, sobriety, and recovery. **Note**: It is possible to relapse to a former phase during this time. ***The "professional addict" believes he has mastered his*** *drug, alcohol, gambling, or sex "habits," but little does he know it has actually mastered him.*

The addict's *supposed* drug mastery is a highlighting factor in the "Advanced Phase." The false confidence in the "addict-identity" is exactly what gets him "messed-up" during this phase. The truth, is many addicts believe they have integrated their "use and abuse" *enough* in their lives to effectively function like a regular human being. But, deep down, they know they *still* have a problem. *Yet*, most addicts *feel* they are in control, when, in reality, they are not. This becomes more and more apparent as time goes on. Thus, marks the beginning of the end for an addict because, at this point, she no longer cares about losing control.

I had over eighteen-years of "use and abuse" experience before I "got clean." And what I learned during those years was how to become a "better addict." In other words, I was moving, but not really moving forward or progressing. Let me take that back - the addiction part of me was progressing and taking more control away from me, but the rest of me was slowly conceding. I had blinders on that blocked my

---

- ADDICT INSIGHT -

"THAT'S THE SAD CONTRADICTION OF A "PROFESSIONAL ADDICT" - THE SAME CONTROL HE BELIEVES HE HAS, IS THE SAME CONTROL HE IS GIVING AWAY TO HIS DOC."

vision, primarily because I did not want to *see* myself giving over control of myself and my life to my "addict-identity." That's the sad contradiction of a "professional addict" - the same control he believes he has, is the same control he is giving away to his DOC.

This loss of control and giving up one's battle against his "addict-identity" defines the addict during the latter phases of substance use disorders. It's almost like a forfeit of life. A "professional addict" eventually submits to a problem that seems greater than himself.

I'm not going to lie to you; during my addict years, I lost hope.

I also tried to care for a "professional addict," who had also lost hope. And it wasn't a pretty sight. That is why doing *everything* you can to prevent an addict from progressing to this phase is of utmost importance. But, if your addicted loved one is already at this point, you, the "helper," **must** proceed like there is a flashing yellow 'caution' sign in front of you.

So, who is a "professional addict?" Well, he is a real danger to himself and others.

Why is a "Professional Addict" Dangerous?

Going from the "Advanced Phase" to the "End Phase" of addiction is dangerous. Addiction triggers reckless confidence, which produces more "use and abuse," which then turns into a reckless dependency on the addict's DOC. Ironically, a "professional addict" foolishly believes she can *still* be functional while continuing to "use." But, the longer the intoxication continues (without treatment), the more ingrained the behaviors become. In other words, the drugs and alcohol not only lull the addict's senses, but it also gives her a false sense of power (control).

I thought I was a functional addict, but I was drowning in "addiction debt." As a result, I tried to find any excuse to use more of my drug of choice as an "escape." Surrendering my independence was a slow process, so slow that I didn't even realize it was happening – that is, until I was fully-dependent on my DOC.

FYI: A fully-dependent addict is a dangerous addict.

Once an addict neglects responsibility for herself - all bets are off. Everything from personal hygiene to daily eating goes up in smoke faster than a crack rock. A person, who doesn't give a damn about herself, or anyone or anything else, is dangerous, but this danger is multiplied when that person is an addict.

Understand that a "professional addict" doesn't care about family, friends, or anyone close to her, because her drug of choice makes all of the decisions. If the "professional addict" has to choose between you and her DOC, she will *choose* the drug. In other words, love doesn't mean anything to a "professional addict."

So, you are in danger if you love or care for this person.

Why? Well, because the person you love or care about loves her drug of choice more than she loves you.

A "professional addict" doesn't care about his safety or health either. From first-hand knowledge, I can tell you that getting to this point takes a considerable amount of drugs and alcohol.

When I was drinking, I didn't care about my current or long-term health. I wanted what I wanted right now in as large a quantity as possible. This is dangerous because accidental overdoses and alcohol poisoning can occur during this time.

Overdose (OD) is when a person consumes an excessive amount of drugs, causing adverse physical reactions. Overdoses are like the consequential gifts from an addicted Christmas. If you don't think the addict in your life will overdose, just give it time. It's almost a foregone conclusion. And it's not just heroin that causes deadly overdoses - a "professional addict" has thought up a variety of creative ways to kill himself – i.e., toxic combinations of alcohol and drugs.

Remember, **addiction is a slow form of suicide, while ODs are the fast-food versions of them.**

The truth is ODs tend to happen with the prideful bunch. You know... the group that wants the new batch of "stuff" - the "stuff" that killed someone last week. Or, the group that feels like their addict experiences and knowledge gives them an extraordinary tolerance against "stuff" that would typically "take out" the "average Joe." This is how a "professional addict" thinks and behaves. But, this way of thinking is flawed, dangerous, and deadly.

Labels and Self-Fulfilling Prophecies

You can count the blades of grass in a field and *still* only have half the number of reasons why people "use and abuse." An addict can state many of reasons for his "use and abuse," but it is usually motivated by low self-esteem and self-confidence. In other words, addicts feel "bad." Now, this "bad" feeling may be real, imagined, or somewhere in-between, but regardless, they *still* feel "bad" about their states of being.

This "bad" may originate from past experiences or stem from present trauma, verbal or physical abuse, mental illness, or depression. However, most of the time, the "bad" comes from internal factors. Yet, most addicts focus on external sources because they are easier to blame. What are the external sources? They are people who experience some type of conflict with the addict. These people also tend to "label" addicts with stigmatizing terms.

This becomes dangerous when a "professional addict" begins to behave like the negative "labels" assigned to her. What is a "label?" "It is a name, title, phrase, or designation given to a person." We "label" people, things, experiences, etc. because it's easy to do. It is also a part of human nature. In fact, with little-to-no effort, we can look at someone, and place her into a category, or we can stereotype someone, so our brains don't have to do too much work. It's easy to "label"; however, it is sometimes much harder to actually get to know someone.

We also "label" people to deliberately hurt them – that is also a part of human nature. Remember, the "stick and stones" song (about hurtful words) from childhood? Well, in this case, "sticks and stones may break our bones and names may hurt us."

In other words, during childhood, we begin to hurl our first insults at others. This behavior continues well into adulthood. The truth is we continue to "label" others to deliberately hurt them. We do this to not only separate ourselves from others but also to come across as "better" than others. So, we can bring people together with "labels," or we can separate them with "labels."

Thus, a "label" can build someone up or tear her down. ***Addicts are bound by the 'labels' assigned to them***. "Labels" can trigger shame, guilt, anger, self-hate, and self-loathing. Sadly, addicts typically get accustomed to being called "no-good-for-nothing-worthless-dirty-lying-filthy-disgusting-hopeless-trash." We have no choice but to get used to the name-calling.

Still, being called horrible names day-in-and-day-out demeans a person, just as much as the drug abuse. Yet, we are forced to wear these negative "labels" like clothes. So, as the addiction progresses, we move from despising these "labels" to embracing them, submitting to them, and finally accepting them. The problem is after an addict begins to wear these "labels" proudly, it increases his risk of actually living out the "labels" (self-fulfilling prophecies)

What is a self-fulfilling prophecy? "It is a false definition of a situation that evokes new behaviors - behaviors that make the original false conception come true." (Merton, 1948).[11] In other words, it is a positive or negative "label" that occurs when a false assumption comes true. ***An abuser becomes a "professional addict" when she self-fulfills most, if not all, of the negative" labels" assigned to her.***

For example, a man who never meant to become an addict begins misusing his pain pills. This supply of pills runs out, and drug-seeking behaviors start. Why? Because he has developed a physical dependency on them. Then, society "labels" him "an addict." His "addict-identity" has over-

---

11. Merton, R. K. (1948). The self-fulfilling prophecy. Antioch Review, 8 (2).

shadowed the person he once was. As a result, his behaviors continue to worsen as the addiction progresses.

The truth is moving from one "Phase of Addiction" to the next creates dysfunction, and then resentment from the addict's family and friends. *Remember, those closest to the addict suffer the most.* These family and friends call their addicted love one every harsh name in the book out of sheer frustration and anger.

The thing is negative "labels" tend to cause this negativity to be internalized, accepted, and then executed (acted upon). Therefore, it is crucial to understand that these "labels" make an addict believe she is a "messed-up addict" – just like everyone else thinks. Because of this mentality, she becomes what everyone says: a "messed-up addict (self-fulling prophecy). In other words, it causes the addict to shoot back, "I'll show them what a 'messed-up addict' really looks like!" *So, remember this...*

"Labels" = Stigma = Low Self-Esteem = Self-Pity = Drug/Alcohol Abuse Excuses

How to Help a "Professional Addict"

Let's be real; you don't want your addicted loved one to get to this point. It's heartbreaking to watch the very life being sucked-out of your loved one. It's almost like the person you knew has become a character on "The Walking Dead" television show. I can relate. But you can help a "professional addict" by applying what you've learned about addiction debt, and using ARM: Accept, Redirect, and Motivate to stop "enabling" behaviors. If you do this, you may be able to stop the progression from "addict" to "professional addict." However, if your addicted loved one has already reached this point, you must take a more drastic pro-active approach.

1. Remove or Change the "Labels"

Years of counseling and "dealing" with everyone from southern bikers to suburban housewives to NYC drug dealers has taught me that people are way more than just restrictive "labels." More specifically, a "professional addict" is more than just an experienced "user and abuser."

So, any redeeming qualities she possesses gets buried under the negative behaviors and associated "labels." As a result, it may seem that the wrong "labels" are promoted the same way boxing bouts are promoted for entertainment purposes. These "labels" become a self-fulfilling in an untreated SUD. So, how can you help an addict? A great place to start is by *getting rid of unfair "labels."* If you can do this, you'll have a better chance of changing how your addicted loved one sees herself.

2. Change Your Language

A "professional addict" is a seasoned veteran in the "use and abuse" world. She has earned a lot of negative "labels" and acquired a relatively thick skin. As a result, your approach should be honest and direct and conscious of the power that negative "labels" can have on her.

The goal is for your loved one to be receptive, so negative "labels" (i.e., "no-good addict") that were assigned to her in the past should either be removed or replaced with more positive ones. You may have given "labels" to others in the past to remind them they are a "no-good-addict," but that must change. Either remove the negative "labels" or change them to more positive ones. Period.

Instead of using terms like "dirty addict," use the term "substance use disorder." Also, replace the negative "label," "lying-no-good-thief," with "a person-in-need-of-help." Go with what works for you but be aware that negative "labels" don't help anything. Rather, the best way to help an addict is to avoid using negative connotations to describe or "label" her.

Realistic and positive "labels" just may be the grease that eases a "professional addict" into actually listening to you.

Once the addict is open to listening to you - other forms of assistance will be easier for her to swallow. But, if you can't avoid "labeling" your addicted loved one, try assigning a few positive "labels" to her. Remember, the goal is for the positive "labels" to outweigh the negative ones.

3. Hold the Addict Accountable

The good news is, changing or removing "negative labels" can help open a "professional addict's" closed door. It's kind of like the saying, "You can catch more flies with honey than vinegar." Well, the truth is being more positive can help you achieve the next step in this challenging process.

During the latter "Phases of Addiction," the addict often lacks being held accountable for her actions. During these phases, patterns of "use and abuse" transform into "everyday rituals." Then, the addict's accountability goes right out the window, and her family and friends lose their motivation to hold her accountable for her actions.

Thus, you must hold the "user and abuser" accountable every time her intoxication leads to negative consequences – for the addict and her loved ones. ***Addicts progress through the various "Phases of Addiction" the same way they go through the "Stages of Change."***

The thing is most "professional addicts" have been in-and-out of the "Contemplation Stage" by this time. During the "Preparation Stage, some have even made some changes. Therefore, the goal of accountability is to push addicts towards the "Action Stage of Change."

What is considered "accountability?" Well, accountability refers to holding someone *responsible* for his actions. Responsibility is a big deal in the substance abuse field. The

The Stages of Change

Fig. 6: The Stages of Change (The Transtheoretical Model, developed by Prochaska and DiClemente)

truth is addiction specialists go through school and get paid to hold addicts accountable for their actions.

It's a difficult but rewarding job. However, it can be difficult for family members and friends, who are just trying to help their addicted loved ones, to understand. But, thankfully, this book was designed to help people just like you! So, what's next? As I said above, so stop "labeling" and name-calling addicts out of frustration. Instead, only call the addict out on his destructive behaviors.

I suggest you focus on the following actions:

1. Getting an addict to assume responsibility for his actions

2. Understanding the role the addiction is playing in the addict's life and behaviors

3. Determining what the addict can do to make-up for these behaviors and actions

4. Give the Addict Ultimatums!

Accepting responsibility for one's intoxicated actions is a big step toward sobriety and "recovery." However, most "professional addicts" appear to be "allergic" to this step.

If you continue to get vigorous resistance from a "professional addict," Beware that this behavior *could* worsen, leading to more drastic measures. *Still*, this is the time to give the addict ultimatums, based on his behavior. What kind of ultimatum? A final demand. You can say something like, "Either you do this, or I will do this."

Remember who you are "dealing" with. Also, acknowledge the life-or-death situation that occurs during the "Advanced" and "End Phases of Addiction." **Note**: You will be giving the ultimatum to a seasoned addict, so proceed with caution. Then, be abrasive and direct.

You can give an ultimatum, but also have the stomach to follow through on it. In other words, you must be 100% committed to this ultimatum. Because if you're not, a "professional addict" *will* take advantage of your lack of commitment.

You can even replace the things (i.e., money, people, belongings, etc.) you lost to "addiction debt" with this ultimatum. For instance, if an addict lives with you, add that into the ultimatum. If you help the addict pay for her bills, add that into the ultimatum. And, if the addict loves having sex, add that into the ultimatum too! Include anything in the ultimatum that the "professional addict" wants and enjoys. This step is easy and hard at the same time. The good news is I am providing a general ultimatum statement for you to use with the addict:

If you don't _____ then you leave me no choice, but to _____.

The Start of the Ending

What may start off like a simple bike ride can become a hellish trip on an uncontrollable locomotive. That last anal-

---

- ADDICT INSIGHT -

"A 'PROFESSIONAL ADDICT' DOESN'T CARE ABOUT YOU. SHE DOESN'T CARE ABOUT ANYTHING - NOT EVEN HER OWN LIFE."

---

ogy is a very elementary description of the ride a substance abuser takes when becoming a "professional addict." That is why extreme effort should be made towards preventing a "user and abuser" from becoming a "professional addict."

The truth is we, as a society, don't know how to deal with addiction effectively. We "label," demean, and stigmatize people with drug and alcohol problems, adding more fuel to the fire. I know... I know...most have earned their "labels" and wear them like "Medals of Honor." But, a "professional addict" eventually leads to the "End Phase" of addiction. During this phase an addict has become too entrenched in this self-imposed mire to save himself. With life in full disarray and submission, the drug of choice only digs its claws deeper into its "host."

But, if you wonder if the addict in your life is a "professional addict," just ask him how his day went. If the addict answers the question honestly, directly, and bluntly and says, his day was either good or bad, based on how much drugs and alcohol, could score - so he wouldn't get "sick," your loved one is a "professional addict." Also, keep in mind that at this stage, addicts have no shame in their games. It's a sad, but undeniable fact that *a "professional addict" doesn't care about you. She doesn't care about anything - not even her own life.*

A "professional addict" always has their finger on the trigger, ready to put a quick end to the addiction's slow form of suicide. ***Therefore, a fully-dependent addict is a very, very dangerous addict.***

The before mentioned is the most dangerous type of addict and should be treated as such. It's almost like you have to watch over your addicted loved one while protecting yourself against her at the same time. So, do not get "caught up" in the addict's shit storm. Keep a safe distance while not "labeling" the addict. Hold her accountable for her actions/ behaviors and giving her ultimatums as a final motivational push. The danger an addict puts herself in is not and should not be a requirement for love.

But, understand that you can't make the addict care or change. The "professional addict" will only change when she becomes "sick and tired" of being "sick and tired." For-tunately, knowledge aids in producing change, so explain to your addicted loved one how she fits into the current "phases of addiction."

The truth is the "End Phase," in particular, can be scary for the family and friends. However, "professional addicts "don't scare easily. ***So, tell your addicted loved one that you refuse to travel with him to this final des-tination***. Hopefully, this will hit the addict with a fist-full of sense. You can't *save* the substance abuser – he has to save himself. However, you can gauge where your addicted loved one's commitment is by letting him explain how he plans to save his own life. After that, wait to see if he follows thru with his dedication to recovery.

Offer to help, even if you think the addict will refuse it. Offering treatment assistance will help clear your conscience. However, if the addict refuses your help, play your ultimatum card. ***Provide information and resources, offer treatment assistance, and use ultimatums, if need be. Then, wipe your hands clean.***

At this point, you have done all you can do to help your addicted loved one or friend. Remember, your addicted loved one's life is ***not*** in your hands, even though most "professional addicts" will try to make you feel that way.

"Professional addicts" will also try to make it seem like they are cannot choose to seek treatment. However, by this point, a "professional addict" is fully aware of his or her loss of control to an "addict-identity," leading to conflicting emotions. Understand that for most of us, emotions affect our thoughts, and thoughts affect our actions and behaviors. It's no different for addicts. Their addictions are also deeply rooted in emotions. It's even possible that the negative "labels" assigned to addicts help "gas-up" negative emotions, which lead to addictive behaviors and mindsets.

I've been "labeled" many things throughout my life. Surprisingly, however, it was not the "addict" title that shamed me the most... But I'll delve into exactly that was in the next chapter. Just remember that a "professional addict" will experience repeated "lows" if her behavior does not change. Some may refer to these "lows" as "hitting rock bottom."

There Is No Rock Bottom

All drugs are a waste of time…They destroy your memory and self-respect and everything that goes along with your self-esteem. They make you feel good for a little while, but then they destroy you. They're no good at all.

— Kurt Cobain

1967 - 1994

(Cause of Death: Suicide by Shotgun & High Amounts of Heroin and Diazepam in His System)

Rock Bottom?

If left untreated, addiction is a terminal disease.

And, just like any other terminal disease, it has an "end-stage" marked by sure signs and symptoms. But, by this point, a "professional addict" has a set routine of "use and abuse" that keeps him out of the "withdrawal stage." Your addicted loved one may not want to admit this, but once a DOC routine has been set, getting "high" becomes less appealing. He continues to drink alcohol and do drugs because he just doesn't want to get sick – i.e., the "shakes" or seizures. The things addicts do for drugs and alcohol are almost as bad as the things drugs and alcohol do to them. In other words, a "professional addict" often does *nasty* things with *nasty* people to get his or her DOC. This is what "non-addicted" people often refer to as "hitting rock bottom."

The term "rock bottom" is commonly used in the substance abuse and recovery world, so much so that it is has become a cliché. When people use this term, refer to someone who has hit the deepest depth of his misery. It's a point of despair, in which he is unable to go any lower - a point of no return.

If you are familiar with addicts, you know that left to their own devices, their bar continuously dips lower and lower. I can tell you from experience, as an "addict," "enabler," a man in recovery, and counselor to those with SUDs - ***there is no rock bottom.***

There Is No Rock Bottom...

Because addicts almost always do what they say they'll *NEVER* do!

Never Say Never

"***Never***" is a term that *most* substance abusers say time-and-time again. For example, "I ***never*** thought I would do this..." Or ***never*** thought I would do that..." These are trademark "addict" statements. For instance, you can literally take an addict's "I'd ***never*** thought I'd..." statement, fill in the blank with whatever craziness you could imagine, and come out with a true statement for many of them.

It's only logical that someone with a chronic disease (like addiction) will make impulsive, manipulative, and ritualistic mistakes – mistakes that help him slowly kill himself – mistakes that he told himself and others he'd **never** do – like becoming an alcoholic or drug addict.

The truth is saying "**never**," as an addict, is just one more sign that he is becoming a "professional addict." In other words, you are merely witnessing your addicted loved one do the exact thing he said he'd **never** do. Well, that thing he said he'd never do – he did in the blink of an eye. Once a "**never**" is committed, it must be a bright red STOP sign to seek immediate help!

Honestly, I **never** thought I'd turn into my "only-sober-when-I'm-asleep-father." I witnessed my father's drunken behavior and thought I'd **never,** in a million years, become a screaming drunk in the streets like he was. Don't get me wrong; my father was more of a spectacle than a walking disaster, but his comical and embarrassing behavior worsened over time. It became an unfortunate thing to see. But for me - I always said, "That won't *ever* be me. I'd **never** act like him!"

Well, I bet you can guess what happened when I grew up? Yeah, I turned into my father. My addiction led me down a road that caused me to become a worst drunk than my father – even at his worst points. I took my father's behavior to a whole other level. I wasn't just a screaming drunk in the streets, no, I was a screaming drunk who walked into traffic and cursed at anyone (even kids) who passed by me. I was a screaming drunk, who periodically lost his voice from screaming at people to fight me.

My "use" eventually led to a "messed-up" body - so "messed-up" I could no longer hold my bladder or bowel movements. If my pants weren't already urine-soaked, I was pissing or shitting in a corner if I couldn't make it to a restroom.

The thing is, I *never* thought I'd be a sloppy, reckless loser. I *never* thought I'd wind up with three DUIs. But I was wrong. After all the shit I lost after the first DUI, I told myself I would *never* get a second one. But I did. Then, after experiencing all that bullshit again - multiplying my losses - I vowed *never* to get a third DUI. But I did. Like countless other drunk-driving Americans before me, I became a repeat offender.

Did you know that one-third of drunk drivers are repeat offenders (Fell, 1995)?[12] It's true. And, in my case, it was almost like I was trying to prove myself wrong by doing what I told myself I would *never* do or *never* do again.

---

12. Fell, J. (1995). Repeat DWI offenders in the United States. Washington, DC: National Department of Transportation, National Highway Traffic Safety Administration Traffic Tech, 85.

- ADDICT INSIGHT -

"THE INSTANT THERE IS A MISMATCH BETWEEN AN ADDICT'S WORDS AND ACTIONS, USE HIS OWN WORDS, AS A WEAPON, AGAINST HIS ADDICTION."

Over time I learned that the saying "never say never" is one of the most real things I have ever heard. Truthfully, though, I had no choice, but to become accustomed to the saying. My *"nevers"* were just like that of other addicts, who were in the "advanced phases" of their addictions. *The reality is "using and abusing" takes people on rides to places they never intended to go. Most don't realize they are even on a trip until they have already gone too far.*

Every time I committed one of my *"nevers,"* I should have checked myself into the nearest treatment center. And I shouldn't have been released without a doctor's approval. It may seem crazy that I did not notice the discrepancies in what I said I'd **never** do and what I actually did, but that's just an addict's way. But guess what? It's also a way for you to help your addicted loved one kick her "habit."

So, how can you use "nevers" to help an addict kick her "habit:"

1. Emphasize Inconsistencies & Discrepancies

The things I was doing were inconsistent with what I said I'd **never** do. These inconsistencies were invisible to me, but not to those around me. So, if you are the "helper" and witness these inconsistencies daily, use them against your addicted loved one. Calling out the inconsistencies is what we, counselors, and other mental health specialists, refer to as "developing discrepancies." What does that mean? It means you present the addict with facts or detailed examples that show how she has deviated from what she said she would **never** do. More specifically, show her how she has shifted from what she said she'd **never** do with concrete proof – i.e., her actions.

By this point, a "professional addict" can pretty much manipulate anyone to gain her drug of choice. Like I stated in Chapter 2, an addict hurts loved ones and friends through her words - words that are used, as weapons, to manipulate people and situations. So, objectively consider your loved one's actions when deciding how to deal with her effectively. The instant there is a mismatch between an addict's words and actions, use her own words, as a weapon, against her addiction.

However, don't be judgmental. So, in a non-judgmental way, highlight the inconsistencies between your addicted loved one's words of **never** doing something and the ways she did exactly that. Also, keep in mind that tone, context, timing, and location are critical elements needed to high-light the differences between her words and actions.

I don't want to come across as a judgmental, nagging asshole, so I always try to use an approachable, non-confrontational tone, time, and setting to talk to addicts. So, I'm asking that you refrain from being combative. It is important to be approachable and "safe" for the addict. More so, an addict needs to feel comfortable, so she is open to receiving your message.

I once had a client, for confidentiality purposes, we'll call her Beth. Well, Beth was in the "Contemplation Stage of Change." She described herself as a cocaine addict and self-referred for treatment because she wanted to quit. Beth reported that she was a high-functioning addict because she was able to maintain a high paying job while still being "coked-up."

However, during our individual and group sessions, she never missed an opportunity to be condescending towards other people's DOCs. In her mind, cocaine was on a higher level in the "substances of abuse hierarchy," causing her to look down upon alcoholics, "pill poppers," and lowly crackheads. She would say, out of spite, "Well, at least I'm not hooked on crack. I would **never** sink that low."

Well, after about a month-and-a-half, Beth ended treatment because she decided she no longer needed it. In her mind, she now had control of the addiction and could resume her normal life.

About a year later, I spoke with another client; we'll call him, John, about Beth. John reported that he had been in the previous treatment group with Beth and that she was "using" again. John also stated that they shared the same drug dealer. And, that drug dealer was selling crack to Beth. John shared that he caught Beth smoking crack one day. I corroborated John's story when she later returned to the treatment group, albeit court-ordered. Because of the drug use (heavy crack use), she looked about ten-years-older and 50-pounds lighter than before.

Beth was once again assigned to me, and that is when the memories of her condescending behavior came rushing back – i.e., the declarations of how she'd "never" sink so low as to smoke crack. Well, this time around, she was in a much more fragile place. It was apparent that Beth was also suffering from poor self-esteem, because in the past, she seemed to feel better about herself after she put others down. I didn't want to kick Beth while she was down with

---

- ADDICT INSIGHT -

"I SPENT SO MUCH TIME AT 'ROCK BOTTOM' THAT I WAS CHARGED RENT FOR STAYING THERE."

"look-at-you-now" type counseling because it would have just made her feel worse.

How did I handle this situation? I strategically used "discrepancy" techniques to point out her behaviors. The truth is, at the time, Beth had a lot of issues – issues that eventually led to a couple of relapses. However, the only counseling method that seemed to have some form of impact had her address the discrepancies between her words and actions.

There Is No Rock Bottom...

because the bottom keeps getting lower and lower = humiliation, embarrassment, and degradation

I've heard thousands of addiction stories about falling and losing things. In the counseling field, it's easy for a professional to become desensitized and burned-out from all of the heartbreaking stories. However, one of the most common themes is "hitting bottom."

It goes a lil something like this:

A person comes in contact with his substance of abuse - this "use" turns into "misuse," which leads to "abuse," which, in turn, progresses into a "dependency." What happens next? This dependency on drugs or alcohol leads to unintended "consequences." Suffering from the consequences and repercussions of substance abuse is considered a "low," and as a result, this "low" leads to more "abuse." Then, the cycle repeats, and the "lows" keep getting "lower."

Let's revisit Beth's addiction story. Beth sniffed coke behind closed doors while looking down upon other crack-heads with her own powdery nose. She said that she'd "***never***" hit rock bottom by smoking crack but later found herself "blowing" the highest bidder just to score a few dollars for a pea-sized rock of it. For her, the "bottom" kept getting "lower."

Another story that I've heard repeatedly is the "gateway" scenario. A client of mine, we'll call him, Michael, began his descent into drug addiction by occasionally smoking a lil weed. He had sworn up-and-down he'd **never** touch the harder stuff because that would be his version of "rock bottom." Well, Michael was later introduced to the harder stuff, because a lil weed just wasn't doing it anymore. As a result of using the harder stuff, a new door opened – one that led directly to a broader drug culture, complete with a lot of other illicit shit. Michael's "rock bottom" kept getting "lower" and "lower" until it felt like there was no "bottom."

Then, there's the story of my "scared of needles" client; we'll call her Jane. Jane vowed to "***never*** shoot-up H," because that would mean the drug outweighed her fear of hitting "rock bottom."

Well, one day, Jane found herself lying on a nasty bathroom floor in a disgusting graffiti-filled stall. What was she doing in there? She was trying to clean a used needle with germ-filled toilet water, so she could "shoot-up H." Like all of the others, Jane's "rock bottom" just kept getting "lower" and "lower."

I spent so much time at "rock bottom" that I was charged rent for staying there. The truth of the matter is, my intoxicated tales are just sad jokes that get worse as they progress. My "rock bottom" plunged each time I experienced a negative outcome. I felt like I was a movie stuntman crashing through floor-after-floor in an old house, mistakenly thinking I had hit the "bottom" each time.

After a while, I would hit what I thought was "rock bottom," only to continue falling. When I think about it, hitting "rock bottom" reminds me of losing your virginity - you never forget your first time. My first time hitting "rock bottom" was at the age of 18, while stationed in Fort Dix, NJ. As you probably guessed, I was in the military at the time. Well, after duty one day, I rode around with one of my "battle buddies," blasting Tupac, and drinking cheap beer and even cheaper *Mad Dog 20/20s*.

Then...

I woke up wearing my underwear in the barrack showers with my company commander and lieutenant desperately trying to snap me out of my first blackout. But, because the cold shower didn't work, my superiors thought I was going to die, so they called EMS for assistance. Up until that point, I'd **never** experienced such embarrassment. I also had **never** witnessed disappointment in the eyes of the people I respected the most. I remember feeling like a piece of shit - like I was "unredeemable." I really believed I had hit "rock bottom," but I hadn't. I was young and naïve at the time, so I had no ideas of the plunges I would take.

But, as I got older, I still didn't know any better. The truth is, I could write a few bestsellers on my "rock bottom lows." During that time, I was averaging a couple of "rock bottoms" a year. I was hitting so many "rock bottoms" that I honestly lost count. And guess what? I didn't learn a damn thing from most of them. That's the insanity of addiction.

Short-term memory + "hard-headedness" + doing the same thing over and over again and expecting different results = addiction

I remember bits and pieces of some of my "lows," but my recollection of the other "lows" comes from friends' accounts or police reports. One of my "rock bottom lows" consisted of waking up in a ditch with a gash and bloody forehead, having my wallet emptied out, and walking around smelling like a putrid combo of piss and sweat. I was so drunk that I stumbled into a pit and fell asleep after security kicked me out of a nightclub. I don't remember any of that because I had blacked out, but that is what I'm assuming happened.

I still have a slight scar on my forehead from that night. The thing is I have always been a vain man, so at the time, that scar made me feel disfigured. I figured I couldn't go any "lower" because the physical, financial, and emotional scars were hard to swallow. But I was wrong.

Another "rock bottom low" for me was being stabbed in the hand by one of my girlfriends and getting locked-up because I tried to defend myself. Good thing I had another girlfriend (on the side) who could bail me out. To be fair, my "other girlfriend" was probably why my "official girlfriend" stabbed me in the first place – I'm not sure. My memory is still a little cloudy when it comes to what actually caused the fight. I was either drunk or "high" at the time, but I do remember laughing as the blood slid down my arm as I examined my sliced-open hand.

I don't remember if that was my first time going to jail; however, I do remember that it was the first time I went to jail and felt like I was never getting out. There is nothing as sobering as hearing heavy steel doors clink as they lock behind you. I really believed that I couldn't go any "lower." I was wrong again.

And Lower...

Jail & Imprisonment

Of course, there would be other times I got locked-up. Incarceration is a typical "low" for most addicts. I talked a little about incarceration in the **Addiction Debt** chapter, but I want to revisit it now since many addicts end up in jail repeatedly.

Addicts lose a lot to "addiction debt." It leads many addicts to jail or prison, which for the majority of them, is their "bottom low." The loss of family, friends, income, self-respect, and freedom get wrapped up together in a dysfunctional cocktail. From the "strip searches" that involve squatting and coughing and "dinner trays" that hold what looks like hot cat food to being stripped of the basic privileges others take for granted, being incarcerating is a sobering experience. So, sobering, you'd expect it to be an addict's "low" or "rock bottom," but sadly, it's usually not.

In other words, the first stint in jail or prison is usually not the last for an addict. But, that first stint in jail or prison is traumatizing, regardless of who you are or what you did to get there. Although jail is generally reserved for minor offenses, it is also used as a holding area for those awaiting trial for major crimes. For many addicts, it is this mix of hardcore inmates and an unrelenting fear of being assaulted by *both* guards and inmates that makes them believe that they have hit "rock bottom."

But wait, it gets worst...

There is also a fear of the unknown. This fear provides an addict with a humbling realization that he has no choice but to obey the guard's orders. It is also a feeling of being *powerless* because he no longer controls himself and his life. It has been taken away from him. In other words, this addict no longer controls what happens on the inside or the outside. Most people would say that being incarcerated is most definitely their "rock bottom," but not an addict. That's not a "rock bottom" for most addicts – regardless of how frightening and humbling the experience is.

The fact of the matter is most, if not all addicts, get used to being incarcerated, especially if they are on their way to becoming "professional addicts." After so many stints in jail or prison, it somehow becomes more comfortable. Then, the bar slips even "lower." In other words, jail or prison becomes commonplace for addicts with each stint in the "big house" feeling like just another day at the office.

What was once a "bottom low" is now just a minor inconvenience or setback. As the addiction progresses, a "professional addict's" minor offenses mature into major offenses. While he may start off in jail, eventually, with repeated drug "use and abuse," he enters the prison system, where those, who commit major crimes are housed for more extended periods – sometimes even for decades. Prison presents a whole new set of "lows," as the stay gets longer, and the clientele gets rougher.

And Lower...

Homelessness

Every time I found myself homeless, that was a "rock bottom low" for me. Similar to incarceration, homelessness is a standard "low" that many addicts experience. Unfortunately, most visit and revisit this form (homelessness) of "rock bottom," just like they visit and revisit jail or prison.

Ironically, addicts will often share war stories and argue about which "low" is the "lowest" - incarceration or homelessness. In my opinion, being homeless is the "lower" experience. Why? Because homelessness seems just as hopeless and demeaning as incarceration...maybe even a bit more because ***poverty is "damning."***

There is no worse feeling of being "damned" than being stuck without food, shelter, clothing, and a pot to piss in.

When you are in jail or prison, you are given food, shelter, clothing, and community pots to piss in, but when you are homeless, you have nothing. When you are homeless, you are just happy to get those basic things. In jail, you get 2 to 3 meals a day. You get to take a shower and sleep in a warm bed, albeit behind bars, but it still beats sleeping on park benches, especially during the winters. The downside of going to jail or prison? Correctional officers look down at you and the other inmates. However, when you're homeless, *everyone* looks down at you... or, at least, it feels that way.

For me, it was the shame that set it apart – the shame of not having anywhere else to go. This "low" made me feel "lower" than dirt. The shame was unbearable, almost like taking a long torturous road trip with a full bladder and no bathrooms in sight.

I was more ashamed of myself than anything else. Here I was, an able-bodied man asking for a bed at a shelter, feeling guilty and ashamed of myself. I did not feel these emotions after becoming intoxicated and cursing at senior citizens in public. All of my drunken episodes, high escapades, and disorderly belligerent conduct did not elicit the same amount of shame as having to live out of a cardboard box.

Homelessness is physically uncomfortable.

When you are homeless, you are tired, weary, dirty, and hungry – all of the time. You hold onto your precious belongings because you don't have much, but eventually, those belongings become *burdens* – reminders of how far you've actually fallen.

Another "rock bottom low" came when my 1997 Jeep Cherokee was towed away with all my belongings inside. I was living out of my Jeep at the time. Paradoxically, my Jeep was towed because I didn't have money to pay for its current registration.

That SUV was a Godsend for me during those days. But, living out of my Jeep was hard, especially when it was cold outside. I still remember being cramped up in a fetal position, desperately trying to keep my body warm within the Jeep's metal frame. Where were all of my family and friends? Not there. There weren't any helping hands available, and my ability to save money was limited – very limited.

I thought I couldn't get any "lower," but once again, I surprised myself. I went from sleeping in my Jeep to sleeping in parks, once the police towed my Jeep away. Let me be real with you; sleeping on park benches is both emotionally and physically painful. My only friends at that time were uninvited roaches and rats just looking to steal my food. I quickly grew tired of this situation. Once I had had enough, I swallowed my pride and walked to the nearest homeless shelter. I went there mainly for sleep because a floor and blanket were a step-up. I thought I could go no "lower." But once again, I was wrong.

Another "rock bottom low" was going from having my own midtown Manhattan office, where I could do whatever my heart desired in, to being homeless and standing in line at a midtown Manhattan homeless shelter, waiting for food.

Can you see the irony of it all?

Addiction cost me almost everything I had, including my dignity. My drug of choice put me on the streets and in shelters. And, let's be real, the "shelter experience" sucks. It was hard for me to accept that I had fallen so "low." And, when I compared my previous life to my current one, I felt even "lower." For instance, an inviting bachelor's pad vs. the uninviting smell of over fifty men's body odors....the cleanliness of my private residence vs. the pubic-hair-laced surroundings of a men's shelter... the warm solitude of my own toilet vs. having to hover over a brown-stained toilet seat that looks worse than anything I'd ever seen. I thought things could get no "lower," but it happened.

Although, for many people, homelessness is a humbling "rock bottom low," it's not the "lowest rock bottom" for an addict. In other words, things can get worse, and they often do. Similar to how addiction progresses and worsens over time, well, consequences like homelessness also worsen with each episode, making an addict feel like he is falling "lower" and "lower." Honestly, for most addicts, the stigma of being "homeless" is far worse than that of being an "addict." That's just one more example of an addict's "messed-up" thinking.

Developing More Discrepancies

You must understand that hitting "rock bottom" is not a one-time event. So, if you take anything from this chapter, let it be an understanding that after each fall to the "bottom," the next one is usually worse, only to be outdone by an even "lower bottom" experience.

So, use this knowledge to stop the addict in your life from future trips to the "bottom." It will save you time and money while also giving you peace of mind. Again, the key is to highlight discrepancies. For example, you could say something like, "Jim, you said this..., however, your actions show this..."

Allow your addicted loved one to explain why there is a mismatch between his words and actions. Also, allow your loved one to explain what he thinks led to this "rock bottom" – the how and why. Remind him that it is the same "rock bottom," he said he'd **never** hit. What is the purpose of highlighting discrepancies? Well, these "bottom lows" are raw moments. And, because these are raw moments, their ear may be more inclined to listen. Therefore, it's the *best* time to talk to your addicted loved one.

But first, it is essential to know the temperament of the person you are trying to help. Why? Well, because knowing his temperament can help you deliver the message in a way he can understand. So, highlight *any* discrepancies (inconsistencies), but focus on the ones causing him to feel ashamed, guilty, unworthy, and defeated.

I felt each one of those emotions during my "lows." And guess what? I still vividly remember those emotions today – how they made me feel.

I cannot stress enough how powerful a weapon "highlighting discrepancies" is. The frustration of doing exactly what you said you'd **never** do is gut-wrenchingly painful. I know I wanted to rip my eyes out with my bare hands to keep from living my "**nevers**." The thing is every drug-fueled bad decision causes an addict to fall deeper and deeper into a hole of despair. The further the fall, the harder it is to crawl back up. It is so frustrating to climb back up and attain a certain status, only to fall back down and have to start all over again.

Honestly, it took many years of repeated trips to the "bottom" before I had had enough. The "lows" just kept getting "lower" and "lower." If you think this is redundant, imagine having to experience "bottom" after miserable "bottom."

And Lower...

Old Highs & New Lows

As I mentioned before, there is no "rock bottom" for addicts because the "bottom" just keeps getting "lower" and "lower." Although these "bottom" experiences are different for each addict and different each time they occur, all "rock bottoms" elicit the same reaction - shame, guilt, a loss of dignity, and self-pity.

I don't know anyone who wanted to become an addict. Regardless of the drug of choice, race, gender, or age – the fall is almost always the same. The beginning is usually the same, as well. A person obtains a "substance" and experiences the desired effects, so she decides to try it again. Now, for some, addiction **nevers** get them in its grasps, but for others, it only takes *one* experience with a drug for addiction to take hold. It is the pleasure, euphoria, boost in libido, etc. that causes people to "misuse" drugs and alcohol. This "misuse" then leads to "abuse," and lastly, a psychological and physical "dependency" on the drug. This may seem simple, but most of the time, nothing is as simple as it looks. Being in a miserable and "low" situation because of drug use seems like a simple equation, but it's not.

Truthfully, an addict will continue to hit new "lows," as he or she moves through the various "Phases of Addiction." These "lows" can be experienced at any phase, but a "professional addict" experiences the brunt of them, especially as she enters the "Advanced" and "End" phases of addiction.

So ultimately, the *only* real "rock bottom" for addicts is death. Then, it's curtains closed. There is nothing you can do to help your addicted loved one at that point. *There's no coming back from death.*

I believe that the term "rock bottom" is too cliché for the average addict. Why? Because it almost makes "being addicted to something" feel *normal,* when it's not even close to that. In other words, it takes an *abnormal,* life-and-death situation and makes it seem like it's no big deal – like it's a joke. But, no one should have to experience the ravages of drug and alcohol addiction.

Ironically, however, this cliché hits home with some addicts. Regardless of the drug of choice, addicts usually get the same result each time – due to their actions. That is the predictability of drug and alcohol abuse. So, pay attention to your addicted loved one's actions, and use them to dictate how you interact with him or her.

So, let's recap:

You now know the true definition of addiction - it's a disease, not a choice. It involves conflict and is a slow form of suicide. I gave you the predictable Phases of Addiction with details into the progression of the disease. You also now know how to recognize the "duality of addiction," so you can help combat a person's "addict-identity." I have also provided you with various coping and problem-solving tools, so you can improve how you communicate with your addicted loved one *and* encourage her to seek help.

I have also given you instructions on how to avoid "addiction debt." And, you've learned what A.R.M is and how to use it to help your addicted loved one. You've also learned how important it is **not** to "enable" the addict in your life.

Moreover, we've reviewed the following: removing and/or changing labels, holding the addict accountable for his actions, and giving ultimatums once the addict progresses towards becoming a "professional addict." Also, I shared with you how to "develop discrepancy," so the addict can see how his words and actions are mismatched.

Addicts must understand there is no "rock bottom." If they know this fact, they'll be less likely to keep falling "lower" and "lower," thinking they've reached the "bottom," when, in reality, there's no such thing – besides death.

By acquiring these skills, you'll be in a better position to help your addicted loved one get "clean" and sober. The goal is to help him reach a turning point, so he'll seek treatment. The good news is hitting "rock bottom" is associated with experiencing "negative consequences." Those "negative consequences" will ultimately lead to a turning point in the addict's life.

CHAPTER 8
The Turning Point

I know those paths of excess, drugs, sex, and alcohol – all those experiences can be funky, they can be very funky, but they're just paths, a diversion, not the answer.

— **Prince**

1958 - 2016

(Cause of Death: *Fentanyl Overdose*)

Do You Remember the Time?

Looking back at my years of "use and abuse," I can't recall *any* good memories. The alcohol either caused me to "black-out," so I did not know what was happening to me or around me, or it tinted *normally* "enjoyable experiences," so my memories of them are distorted. But, what is glaringly apparent is that I had more bad times than good. What is also clear is that the "good times" you see on beer commercials are either fake or involving people who don't have addiction issues. Truthfully, I believe it's fake – just actors and actresses trying to snag a paycheck. Either way, these commercials are misleading.

I was always embarrassed. I remember waking up in a panic because I thought I had spent most, if not all, my money. I did not remember much of what happened the night before; the only way I could determine if I was broke was to check my crumpled-up receipts from last night. I remember waking up wet and smelling like an elevator in an inner-city housing project because I had pissed myself.

I also remember praying that I didn't drunk-dial women or send intoxicated texts to them. Well, I didn't do that... But, in my drunken state, I somehow managed to text hateful things to every female on my "Contacts List." Even more, messed up was waking up in a hospital bed, hoping I didn't kill anyone. The sad thing is this happened many times.

Then, there were more than a few times where I woke up naked next to random women. I remember thinking, "Who the hell is this, and what the hell did I just do?!" Over and over again, I woke up with blood in my mouth, not wanting to swallow my own spit. I woke up in fields, parking lots, and in parks, cold to the bone, and *hating* every second of it. Many times, I was too sick to eat anything, but too hungry to care. By this time, I was a "professional addict."

Researchers and scientists have explored the impact of negative memories on the brain, doing all kinds of experiments, from the loss of money to the loss of whatever it is that rats care about, and found that people are more likely to remember experiences that have negative connotations attached to them (Kensinger, Garoff-Eato, & Schacter 2007).[13] The majority of these studies came to a similar or same conclusion - we remember negative things more because they have a more significant impact on us – more so than the positive things.

But, after years of unpleasant and horrifying memories, and after years of others constantly reminding me of the unpleasant and horrifying memories I caused them, it *still* wasn't enough for me to change course. Well, guess what? There are many more like me - millions of people who are addicted and "hard-headed" - millions who continue to "abuse" drugs and alcohol, despite the negative experiences and memories. Replicas of myself, during my years as an AAA.

Once again, that is the insanity of addiction.

What appears to be a lack of willpower is a "mental deficiency," a disease of the brain, psyche, and spirit. You would think that the unpleasant and horrifying memories would lead to a different outcome, and while that is true for people with "normal brains" people with "addicted brains," process things differently.

_____

13. Kensinger, E. A., Garoff-Eaton, R. J. & Schacter, D. L. (2007). How negative emotion enhances the visual specificity of a memory. Journal of Cognitive Neuroscience 19(11), 1872-1887.

- ADDICT INSIGHT -

"NEGATIVE CONSEQUENCES ARE INCENTIVES FOR ADDICTS TO CHANGE THEIR BEHAVIORS."

In other words, addicts are extremely "hard-headed" people. I hit what I thought was a "rock bottom" too many times to count only to realize it wasn't indeed my "rock bottom."

What should have been a wake-up call only ended-up being a temporary timeout for me. I continued to hit "rock bottom" time and time again.

For addicts, like me, things have to get worse before they even have a chance of getting better.

We not only have to experience the negative, but we also must experience "rock bottom lows" and all of the negative consequences associated with them. That is why substance abuse treatment is so difficult. Drugs and alcohol stimulate the brain, producing pleasurable feelings, and reinforcing addictive behaviors.

"It is this combination of the positive reinforcing effects of the drugs with the reduction of the negative emotional states of drug abstinence that provide a powerful motivational force for the compulsive drug-taking that characterizes addiction" (Koob, 2003).[14] In Chapter 1, I discussed "reward pathways" in the brain and the neurotransmitter, dopamine. I explained how drugs and alcohol abuse is both rewarding and reinforcing at the same time. *This "reward pathway" controls an addict's mindset – and it is this mindset that controls an addict's behavior.* Thus, the goal is for punishment (consequences) to decrease drug-related actions.

The Key to an Addict's Turning Point = Consequences

An addict will not achieve a "clean" and sober recovery without experiencing the consequences of his "use and abuse," this is as certain as death and taxes. For every alcoholic beverage consumed, dope smoked, or pill popped, there are consequences. In the simplest terms, a consequence is an outcome or effect of a prior action or behavior. It's a concluding result. Typical consequences for addicts include poor health, lengthy hospital stays, homelessness, incarceration, the loss of family, friends, and finances, debt, depression, and death. So, as you can see, the main ingredient is the negative. Negative consequences are incentives for addicts to change their behaviors.

---

14. Koob, G. F. (2003). Neuroadaptive mechanisms of addiction: Studies on the extended amygdala. European Neuropsychopharmacology, 13(6), 442 – 452.

As counselors, we receive years of training on detecting addictive behaviors and how to assist others in recognizing these behaviors. Much of our behavioral education is based on operant behavior conditioning, a learning process, initially developed by Edward Thorndike and B.F. Skinner. This learning tool uses punishment and positive and negative reinforcement to increase the probability of specific, more "acceptable" behaviors (Skinner, 1953).[15] In layman's terms, this means that rewards and punishments are used to entice someone to do something – or not do something.

The goal of punishment is to decrease negative behaviors. Let's consider "punishment" as a consequence. In operant behavior conditioning, this is called "discriminative stimuli." This type of punishment takes something away (negative punishment) from a person or gives something to the person that is usually unwanted (positive punishment). These two forms of punishment are called "gains" and "losses." So, regardless if something is "gained" or "lost," the main goal is for an addict to be the sole recipient of the consequence.

Punishments are as varied as motorcycle types, but some are more beneficial to the "turning point" than others. Examples of punishments include withdrawals and hangovers. Withdrawal is a familiar consequence of drug use.

---

15. Skinner, B. F. (1953) Science and human behavior. New York.

Most addicts try to prevent withdrawals by any means necessary. It really is that terrible.

It is this fear of withdrawal that reinforces the continued use of drugs or alcohol. It is this desire to avoid "dope sickness" that prevents addicts from seeking treatment. Thus, dependency not only stems from a desire to get "high," but also to avoid painful withdrawals. That is why your addicted loved one **must** fully experience the consequences of her "use and abuse." In other words, she **must** experience withdrawal to recover from addiction.

But, do not try to force an addict to stop "using" or seek treatment during withdrawal. Wait until it's over, and then try to help her analyze the consequences of the addiction. You may want to video record your addicted loved one in compromising positions or during withdrawal. Why? So, she can see with her own eyes what the addiction has done or is *still* doing to her. An "addict-identity" helps substance abusers to forget unpleasant consequences, but a video recording is something we can't deny.

Note: *Withdrawing from alcohol or benzos can be dangerous and must be medically supervised by healthcare professionals.*

Although withdrawals are uncomfortable, scary, and possibly dangerous, they are a necessary part of an addict's "turning point." More specifically, it's an integral part of taking the drug or alcohol out of the equation. It is also important to note that having too many drugs and alcohol in the system can be too much for the body to handle = overdoses (ODs). ODs are **not** a punishment you want your addicted loved one to experience. Sometimes, an overdose can be reversed, but many times it cannot. Honestly, an OD is just one step closer to death. And, we all know there's no coming back from that.

Understand that the physical and mental consequences of addiction are far-reaching and varied. Drug-related illnesses are no joke. They range from mild-to-severe, short-term-to-long-term, and temporary-to-permanent. The long-term and permanent consequences are sad, but often have a greater impact on the addict, due to the damage they cause.

In other words, brain damage and incurable STDs are more likely to make addicts consider treatment than just bad hangovers or curable STDs. Keep in mind that the most severe consequences begin during the "Anti-Social Phase" of addiction. Similar to how the addiction progresses over time, so does the severity of the consequences. As a drug and alcohol abuser becomes an addict, there is an increased risk of financial ruin, a loss of monetary resources, overdoses, chronic diseases, terminal illnesses, brain damage, STDs, and damaged or destroyed relationships.

To elicit change, an addict must **want** to change. What makes an addict want to change? Well, most of the time, something has to happen for him to see the benefit of changing. In fact, in most cases, an addict has to experience a negative consequence (i.e., a near-fatal overdose, jail or prison, homelessness, etc.) before he realizes something **has** to change. It is usually an uncomfortable or painful situation that evokes so much displeasure that he seriously considers changing because it's a better alternative.

So, the consequence produces positive behavior. ***Therefore, the goal is to use negative consequences to elicit more positive behaviors.*** I like to call these (positive and negative) consequences "rewarding punishments."

Fig. 8-1: "REWARDINGPUNISHMENTS"

The *Most* Rewarding Punishments

- ❖ Loss of People
- ❖ Homelessness
- ❖ Incarceration

1. A Loss of People

People are a drug user's greatest resource to continue getting drugs. A person usually gets his first taste of a drug through his family or friends. Eventually, he learns how to get a hold of alcohol and drugs on his own. And, as addiction sets in, the "substance user" becomes a "substance abuser" and then a "addict." The "user," "abuser," and "addict" need people through all "Phases of Addiction" - from the "Experimental Phase" to the "Remission Phase." People are needed to aid in an addict's self-destruction.

As I've stated before, addiction creates the most selfish individuals on the planet. An addict is narcissistic in all aspects of her life, but you can best believe when she needs help getting that "fix," selfishness towards others goes down the toilet like drugs after a cop bangs on the door.

So, what should you do? Take yourself out of the equation. Understand that you are a resource. *It doesn't matter if you're the spouse, romantic partner, concerned friend, parent, or child, you still bring something precious to the table - something the addict depends on. What do you bring? You bring an "obligation by association."*

It is also critical to understand that those closest to an addict typically feel a duty to assist him, regardless of the circumstances, simply out of obligation. Guilt and fear also contribute to this feeling of obligation. When I ask the families of my clients (the addicts) why they "enabled" their addicted loved ones, they always say, "I felt obligated to help him because he's my son/cousin/friend/spouse/parent/nephew." But, what I hear even more is, "If I don't help him now, I'm going to have to help him later." *You are not obligated to help an addict, especially if he isn't trying to help himself.* You are also not obligated to help an addict simply because of an association. **Never** allow "guilt by obligation" to be the reason you feel responsible for an addict.

Addicts are notorious for "guilt-tripping" their loved ones because they know they will feel guilty and give them money. Addicts "guilt trip" those that care about them so that person will "guilt tip" out of obligation.

Well, guess what? You're **not** responsible for another adult or her decisions. The only person you're required to take care of is a minor – when you're the caretaker. So, I'm only referring to adults.

As an "enabler" (resource), you probably provide financial assistance to the addict in your life. But, when you use the "rewarding punishment" tactic, you take yourself out of the picture, so the addict no longer has financial security. Removing yourself as a human resource becomes a *real* consequence of her continued "use and abuse."

Once you stop assisting an addict, a few things may happen – (1) She may find other ways to get her drug of choice, even if these ways lead to negative consequences like incarceration or homelessness, or (2) she may internalize the negative consequences and come to a realization that a change is needed. But, before you stop helping her, take yourself out of the picture, as a consequence. Then, give her a strong ultimatum and stick by it.

In other words, give the addict an ultimatum, and then step away if she refuses to follow through. This is especially important if she is a "professional addict." Remember, to the addict; you are a "monetary resource," however, financial assistance is not the *only* reason she finds you resourceful. She probably really does love or care for you. Addicts *still* love and care for others; however, they don't love and care for others as much as they love and care for their DOCs.

An addict's family, kids, and even her pets are "resources," so the removal of `them are negative consequences for her. Why does this work? Because these people are *still* vital to her. So, subtracting them, including "helpers," can be a "rewarding punishment" for an addict.

2. Homelessness

Remember, there is no "rock bottom" for an addict because the "bottom" just gets "lower" and "lower." The truth is homelessness is one of the most common "rock bottom lows" of addictive behavior. Give an addict enough time, and he will eventually end-up homeless. If the addict manages to function enough to secure his residence, there is a good chance he will still eventually lose it to addiction. Regardless of whether or not an addict can hold onto his home, there is a high probability that he will ultimately become homeless. So, how should you, the "helper," handle this situation? By using the threat of homelessness as punishment with potential for reward.

When it comes to operant behavior conditioning, homelessness, as a punishment, means removing the addict's stable and secure living environment. As a "helper" and head of the house, you can initiate the negative consequence of homelessness by giving your addicted loved one an ultimatum of either stopping the "drug use" and entering treatment or being homeless.

Even if you are not the head of the household, you can still use this negative consequence to your advantage, because at some point, your addicted loved one will be homeless and in need of a place to stay. That's when she will turn to you.

Not having a stable and secure place to live is rough. It doesn't matter if you are a man or a woman; it's still hard. However, men have egos that tell them that they should be "providers" and able to care for themselves and others, so when they are unable to do that, it's demeaning for them.

Living in a homeless shelter, car, motel, or being out on the streets can inspire an addict to change. It can make him realize he can either continue on this downward spiral through the various "Phases of Addiction" or seek help. As a "helper," you **must** allow the addict to fully experience his actions' negative consequences. Still, you must also be resolved, only intervening if he is in immediate danger. Thus, homelessness can be a "rewarding punishment."

3. Incarceration

As touched upon earlier, punishments can also include stints in jail or prison. Taking away one's freedom is a sobering experience, figuratively and literally. A short-term jail stay may be just enough of a consequence for an addict in the "Anti-Social Phase" of addiction, while a more extended prison stay may be just what is needed for a "professional addict" in the "Advanced Phase" of addiction.

If being jailed or imprisoned is to have the desired impact on your loved one's addiction, you have to let her do the time. So, you should prepare yourself for what will surely come next. She will beg you to pay her fines and bail or find a bail bonds agent for her, **but don't do it**. This negative consequence (punishment) **must** be experienced for her to see the importance of changing.

> # - ADDICT INSIGHT -
> ## "YOU CAN LOVE AN ADDICT, BUT NOT UNCONDITIONALLY, BECAUSE THE ULTIMATE CONDITION IS FOR HIM GET 'TREATMENT.'"

So, let her sit in jail or prison and dine on nasty jail or prison sandwiches day-in and day-out. The idea is to let her feel-live-and breath-in all of the consequences of her actions. But don't believe the hype – jail and prison are **not** as dangerous, as the movies would have you believe.

And, under the right circumstances, incarceration can actually be a *good* thing. This concept is difficult to grasp, for both the addict and those trying to save her. The thing is confinement was **never** supposed to be a positive experience. For thousands of years, regardless of the society, confinement was reserved for punishable crimes. However, over the decades, the meaning of punishment has changed, and confinement has become a go-to term. Fortunately, for some like me, spending time in jail helped me see that something needed to change.

Thus, being "locked-up" is not always a bad thing for those addicted to substances of abuse. Sometimes the best thing that can happen to an addict is to get "locked-up" for a while. It will keep him safe – from himself. ***The irony of it all is while the addict loses his freedom by being*** *in jail or prison, he also gains the tools he needs to recover in that same jail or prison.*

While confined, addicts are forced to conduct inward reflections of themselves, their "use and abuse" and the circumstances that eventually led to the confinement. The truth is being behind bars feels like being put into timeout for an addict. It is a time for the individual to physically and mentally reset.

However, this involuntary get "clean" period **must** be combined with other important elements (i.e., determination, perseverance, along with substance abuse treatment and vocational, educational, and spiritual services) for an addict to abstain from drugs and alcohol upon his release. Surprisingly, these elements can also be found in jails and prisons.

Religion is incredibly easy to find in jail and prison. When all you have is time, regret, fear, and anxiety on your hands, the gospel becomes a welcomed relief - a message of peace or at least a positive distraction from the routine "humdrum" of confinement. Thus, incarceration can be a "rewarding punishment."

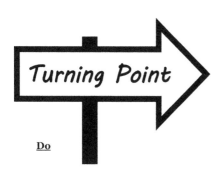

Dos & Don'ts

<u>Do</u>	<u>Don't</u>
☐ Let Consequences Happen	☐ Be His/Her Savior
☐ Encourage Change	☐ "Enable" Him/Her
☐ Practice Empathy	☐ "Guilt Trip" or "Guilt Tip"
☐ Remind Him of His Responsibilities	☐ Assume His Responsibilities for Him
☐ Highlight Discrepancies	☐ Argue with Him/Her
☐ Punish the Behavior	☐ Punish Him/Her for the Addiction
☐ A.R.M. Him/Her	☐ Feel Obligated to Him/Her
☐ Dish-Out "Tough Love"	☐ Give Him/Her Unconditionally Love

Turning Point Dos and Don'ts

❖ **Do** *Allow Consequences to Happen/**Don't** Be a Savior*

In other words, allow your addicted loved one to experience the consequences of her actions - it's **not** something that should be shared between the two of you. Also, don't try to save her from those consequences. Remember, you are not her superhero. Let her be her own superhero and save herself.

❖ **Do** *Encourage Change/**Don't** "Enable" the Addict & Hope for Change*

An addict has to want to change before anything changes. You can encourage this desire to change by offering her positive support, but ***don't*** try to make her change if she's not ready to. Also, ***don't*** "enable" her in any way, shape, or form. Why not? Well, because it's better to do nothing than to "enable" an addict.

"Enabling" an addict with the hope she will change is the equivalent of throwing your hard-earned money overboard on a cruise. Remember, consequences can be "rewarding punishments."

❖ **Do** *Practice Empathy / **Don't** "Guilt Trip" or "Guilt Tip"*

In other words, lend your ear and little else. Be aware of how your addicted loved one feels and why she feels that way. Remember the difference between internal feelings and external actions. Please do not feel guilty and then "guilt tip" (give money to her because you feel guilty that she's in this predicament) because of that guilt.

❖ **Do** *Remind The Addict of His Responsibility for Himself/***Don't** *Assume Responsibility for Him*

Keep in mind that this is his life, so it is his responsibility and *only* his responsibility to look after himself. So, remind him that he has control over his own life and can achieve sobriety if he wants to. **Don't**, however, make things too comfortable for him, or he'll never stop "using."

❖ **Do** *Highlight Discrepancies /* **Don't** *Argue*

Every chance you get, bring attention to the inconsistencies of what the addict says and does. Remind him how his behaviors impact others but ***don't*** beat a dead horse and get baited into endless back-n-forth arguments with him.

❖ **Do** *Punish the Behavior /* **Don't** *Punish the Person*

Keep in mind that addicts suffer from substance use disorders, a diagnosable illness that affects millions, so it is their behaviors, not the people that are the problem. An addict's actions deserve the consequences, not the person. The person deserves empathy and respect, just like everyone else.

❖ **Do** *A.R.M Him or Her/***Don't** *Feel "Obligated by Association"*

"Obligation by association" leads to "enabling." So, replace emotions with actions and "actions of obligation" with A.R.M. = Accept, Redirect, and Motivate

❖ **Do** *Tough Love* / **Don't** *Provide Unconditionally Love*

You can love the person and not his actions. Unconditional love gives the addict the right to do anything and *still* feel entitled to your love. So, don't provide him with unconditional love.

FYI: **You can love an addict, but not unconditionally, because the ultimate condition is for him to get "treatment." He can't do that if he has you to fall back on unconditionally.**

Interventions Don't Work

*Traditional interventions **do not** work.*

You may see family and friends circled around an addict, telling him that it's "treatment or else" on television. In this fantasy world, the addict declares that he will seek treatment, often to appease those crying around him or yelling at him. But, the truth is this type of intervention only works on reality shows. Once an addict leaves the intervention, he will most likely go to score some more drugs. He won't actually seek treatment until he almost dies from an overdose or is court-ordered to do so. Imposed abstinence from substances of abuse is still abstinence, but "clean" time can pose risks.

And, because he is now "clean," his body will lose its tolerance for his DOC. What does that mean? It means that if he decides to drug-binge again or return to "using and abusing" again, his body will not be ready for the drug or alcohol use, possibly causing him to experience an overdose.

So, after months or years of "enabling," do you really think one interventional meeting with some ultimatums of "treatment or else" will get through to your addicted loved one? No, it won't. Remember, to "enable" is to kill, because as an "enabler," you are preventing your addicted loved one from experiencing the negative consequences of her actions.

"Enabling" is the mortal enemy of consequences.

As a society, we focus your attention on the prevention of substance abuse in pre-teens and teens, instead of on interventions that an addict won't even hear. Honestly, traditional interventions often do not work for adult addicts. But, preventions do work with younger kids. So, begin this with younger kids by being bluntly honest with them. More specifically, state flat-out that some Moms and Dads have problems that may get passed down to them.

This is what I told my kids, "Daddy can't drink adult beverages, because it makes him become a 'bad person.' But, Mommy can drink adult beverages because they don't transform her. Because I can't drink adult beverages, you may have the same problem when you are older. So, the best thing for you to do is not even start drinking adult beverages."

Start prevention with your kid at the first signs of substance "use" and **not** when the "use" has progressed into abuse!

Onus on Them

What I've learned as an "addict," "enabler," and counselor is that you can't save a substance abuser who does not want to be saved. When this person is in a bad enough situation or just fed-up, he will make a conscious decision to save himself. But, to finally get to a point when he wants to be saved, the "Turning Point," he **must** fully experience the consequences of his actions. ***The "Turning Point" for most addicts is when they experience unbearable consequences – things they have not become desensitized to.***

In other words, a "Turning Point" occurs once an addict gets sick and tired of being sick and tired. That is when his body breaks down, his will breaks down, and his resolve breaks down. That is when he will be ready to seek treatment.

It is imperative that the consequences or "rewarding punishments" be overwhelming. Why? Because "professional addicts" are impulsive, manipulative, and ritualistic, which means they are not going to change anything if the impact isn't big enough. So, all of your asking, hoping, and praying that things will change will be in vain if the addict doesn't want to change. Put all of that to the side and use the A.R.M (Accept, Redirect, and Motivate) method, my "Turning Point: Dos and Don'ts" checklist, and ultimatums to inspire your addicted loved one to want to do something different. Then, allow him to decide if he wants to change.

While your loved one is deciding whether or not to make a change or *contemplating* what this change will involve, allow him to *feel* the fire of his folly. Regardless of how much you want to protect him from being hurt – he needs to feel the hurt to heal.

In other words, you have to let him feel the consequences.

Letting your addicted loved one *feel* the consequences requires that you don't "enable" him. ***Because to "enable" is to kill, but it is also the mortal enemy of facing the consequences***.

I said it before, and I'll say it again... the hardest thing to do is to do nothing when it comes to saving an addicted loved one from pain. Doing nothing may sound simple, but when it involves someone you love or care about, it can be extremely difficult. The truth is no one wants to be heartless, but your loving care could be the coal to your addict's furnace.

As friends and family of substance abusers, we sincerely yearn for them to get better and live productive lives. *As a society, we must get out of the mindset that only a cold heart gives a cold shoulder. So, remove yourself from the equation and allow your addicted loved one to suffer through the consequences (i.e., homelessness or incarceration).*

It is critical to understand that consequences are catalysts for change, but they are not enough to halt addictive behaviors by themselves. "One and done" is an unfamiliar term to those plagued by the disease of addiction. One consequence can be compared to the flame of a Bic lighter, while multiple consequences can be compared to the flames of a cremation furnace. In terms of "rewarding punishments," multiple ones are more powerful than just one.

To be honest, if one consequence were enough to get addicts to their "Turning Points," then people would stop drinking after their first DWIs or stints in homeless shelters or jails. The thing is "users" do not earn the "professional addict" designation from one single act; no, they gain this title from a reoccurring pattern of abuse. Similarly, reoccurring consequences are often the only things strong enough to convince the most seasoned addicts to change. A "Turning Point" only occurs after cumulative consequences, providing there is enough of an undesired result to make the addict want to change.

So, how can you make someone want to save their own life? You can't. The person must want to be saved. In other words, you can't save your addicted loved one; she has to want to save herself. Remember, a "Turning Point" only occurs once an addict can comprehend the consequences of her actions.

So, it comes down to this - addicts are unable to care about anyone but themselves. When they become "professional addicts," they can't even "muster-up" the strength to care about themselves. The *only* thing that seems to faze them is extreme personal discomfort – i.e., withdrawals, an extended loss of freedom (jail or prison), a loss of anyone who has "helped them" acquire their DOCs, and anyone who gives them "guilt tip" money to purchase drugs and alcohol.

Therefore, use discretion and the lessons you have learned from this book to help you decide when or if you will allow your addicted loved one to suffer through "rock bottoms" – without your assistance. The primary focus is for the addict to experience the "rewarding punishments" due to their drug/alcohol-fueled actions. As a result, consequences can help addicts reach "turning points" in their lives.

CHAPTER 9

Sobriety

Now, not only do I expect to be here, and I'm not going anywhere, but I've had the last 12 years of my life being free of substances to kind of figure out who the substance-free guy is, because he's a different guy. Just by brain chemistry, it can't be avoided. I'm not the same, I don't think the same. I don't react the same. And, my outlook isn't necessarily the same.

— Chris Cornell, Lead Singer of Soundgarden

1964 - 2017

(Cause of Death: *Suicide by Hanging with Four Different Drugs in His System*)

The Sober Process

I define sobriety as abstinence from all substances of abuse, not just alcohol. If a substance abuser lives long enough, sobriety will be one of his goals. Because it's only a matter a time before the addiction makes his life unbearable. ***Take it from me, all dependent relationships with drugs and alcohol end in divorce or death.*** Even with the "messed-up" mindset that comes with having a substance use disorder, self-preservation, in the form of abstinence, will eventually turn into the only viable option for an addict.

Eventually, after all of the punishing consequences, the dim light becomes brighter. As I've stated many times before, an addict has to *want* to be sober to become sober. Truthfully, living sober never really appealed to me. My destructive habit was so ingrained in my life that it felt as much a part of me as riding my motorcycle. To not use a mind-altering substance and be "clean" just seemed *unnatural*. To not "use" was to not enjoy life.

It took me way too long to recognize that I was different - that I was someone who could **not** consume alcohol like other "normal" people.

Surprisingly, after each "rock bottom hit," I debated if I *should* continue "using." But, my "messed-up" way of thinking won out every time. My addict-identity told the rest of me that a sober life was a boring life.

- ADDICT INSIGHT -

"ALL DEPENDENT RELATIONSHIPS WITH DRUGS AND ALCOHOL END IN DIVORCE OR DEATH."

Truth-be-told, I couldn't picture a life without drinking because it brought me so much "joy." Yeah, wet, pissy pants and a mouth full of vomit "joy." Eventually, however, "being sober" went from feeling *unnatural* to being an *absolute must,* yet I *still* viewed it as an "outsider," who desperately wanted to be admitted into an exclusive club.

There are many hard facts regarding addiction, but the most basic one is probably one of the hardest to swallow yet, most important. The truth is, for whatever reason (genetics or environment), an addict can't "use" under any circumstances. It may seem simple to most, but it's a deathly fact for a select few of us vulnerable to drugs and alcohol. Is it unfair? Absolutely! We get it, but we are stubborn people, so this fact alone can cause us to say, "To hell with sobriety!" Then, we continue "using." This hard fact is as important as putting gas in a motorcycle. For an addict to achieve sobriety, "helpers" should make it crystal clear that he cannot "use" under any circumstances. The sooner he realizes this, the better. ***So, explain this to the addict, as simply and directly as possible. Say something like this, "Kevin, the drug's chemical makeup and your physical makeup do not mix, so the terrible effects you have been experiencing are a result of this mismatch."***

After years of hospital stays stemming from car accidents, jail stays because of disorderly conduct, and "sick bed" stays because of hangovers - sobriety just seemed like the better choice than the loaded gun I kept aiming at my face. But, even after the self-inflicted pain I endured, I *still* didn't want to get "clean." In other words, I wasn't too fond of the concept of abstinence. The negative consequences just became too much for me to deal with. But it *still* took me a really long time to get to a point in which I *wanted* to be sober. I got to my "Turning Point" and sobriety through trial by consequence, but with the help of this book, hopefully, others won't have to sit in the same court. ***Remember, for sobriety to be successful, an addict has to want it***. Sadly, however, many addicts do not *want* to be sober - until it's too late.

Thus, as a counselor, my goal is to help others with addictions *want* to, prepare for, and live in sobriety. The good news is if the addict in your life is ready to change, you can appeal to his inner *wants and needs* to make those changes. These *wants* and *needs* are going to inspire him to *want* to live a sober life. They will also be the catalysts that encourage him to begin the "sober process."

The "Wants"

- ❖ Forgiveness
- ❖ Atonement
- ❖ Redemption

We, substance abusers, *want* to do things our destructive habits will not let us do. Many of us *want* to be sober, productive members of society. The great philosophers, John Locke and Jean-Jacques Rousseau, once said, "Humans are genuinely *good*." Well, addicts are also generally *good*.

We are good people who suffer from *bad* conditions. Most addicts don't *want* their loved ones to despise them or be ashamed of them - they *want* and *need* to be forgiven. They also don't *want* to be defined by their intoxicated actions – and they *want* to atone for the things they did during their addictions. So, to sum it up, addicts don't *want* to be living and breathing burdens to their loved ones - they *want* to redeem themselves.

1. Forgiveness

Guilt is a crippling emotion.

It's one of those emotions that eats at your core long after you've committed the sin. Because "getting high or drunk" is one of the most selfish acts a person can do, the guilt that comes afterward is especially crippling. It's like getting an STD after a one-night stand - you have it, and it's always there. It's not going anywhere, so every time you think about it, you feel worse about it and yourself.

Well, as the disease of addiction progresses, so does the guilt. **The more I "used," the more I felt guilty about the things I did, and the more guilty I felt, the more**

I wanted to "use" to ease that guilt. "Forgetting" the guilt became the "high" of "getting high" for me.

I felt guilty about all of the money I spent on my bail - money that *should have* been used to care for my newborn daughter. I felt guilty about the time I wasted on my habit - time I didn't give to my family. I felt guilty that my employers, co-workers, friends, and family – people who depended on me, were pushed to second place by my "liquid lover."

After "messing-up" so many things for so many years, I screwed over too many people. The guilt led to shame. Then, the guilt and shame became too heavy for me to bear, so I numbed my feelings with alcohol. Naturally, addicts *want* to lift that heavy weight off their shoulders. They *want* to be absolved of their "wrongs," and they *want* to be forgiven.

Their actions may say otherwise, but they *want* and *need* your forgiveness. Fortunately, **you** have the power to forgive your addicted loved one for whatever she did. It is **your** forgiveness that will help her forgive herself. **Note: Your** forgiveness is not only an amazing gift but also a very powerful tool, so don't give it out lightly. The requirement for this "gift" should be sobriety.

The Keys to Forgiveness

1. Make it clear to your addicted loved one that you are *willing* to forgive her, but she has to be sober and "clean" for you to give that "gift" to her.

2. Encourage your loved one to admit her guilt. Sobriety is based on brutal honesty and openness. So, address exactly what she is guilty of doing, then forgive her for that *exact* "thing" (if you can) and *only* that "thing."

3. Forgive, but don't forget and make sure she doesn't forget either. "Forgetting" the "wrongs" can lead to you being manipulated in the future, so your loved one needs to be reminded of what she did, so she's not prompted to "slide back into old habits."

2. Atonement

I *wanted* to be forgiven, and I also *wanted* to make amends for all of the grief I caused others while in my "drunken states." The truth is addicts *want* to right their "wrongs." So, fan the flames of desire for atonement to ignite sobriety. The *want* to be forgiven, and the *want* to atone are related like *Harleys* and leather.

My sister, who often stole my belongings to support her crack habit, was always trying to pay me back for what she took. At times, it seemed like she would do *almost* anything to please me. This was her way of trying to atone for her actions.

Big sis honestly believed that she could make amends if she could "pay" me back for what she took from me. She never told me she was trying to make amends for the things she stole for crack, but I knew why she was doing it.

*However, for the atonement to be successful, an addict **must** follow the three steps listed below:*

The Keys to Atonement

1. Make your addicted loved one acknowledge the action he *wants* to atone for. This step goes back to being honest and open, which are the keys to starting the "process of sobriety."

2. Praise him for *wanting* to make amends. Just by him *wanting* to atone, he shows you that he is ready to change his mindset. So, encourage him and praise him for taking this step. The truth is there is not much addicts get commended for, so any positive action should be applauded.

3. Have him repay the "wrong(s)" he *wants* to atone for. For instance, if your addict husband steals, then pawns your tv for Xanax pills, make him make amends for that theft – i.e., purchase a new television for you. So, be clear about what the "wrong" is and what he can do to repair the damage.

Amends **must** be made.

And, your loved one must acknowledge why he is making amends because this acknowledgment is just as important as making the amends in the first place. *Sobriety is an action-based process.* I call this part, "show & prove." This is the first step; if your loved one *wants* to show that he *wants* to be sober, he proves that *want* through his actions. Atonement provides an addict with something to work towards - a constructive activity that occupies his time.

3. Redemption

Being forgiven and making an atonement can lead to redemption.

If a substance abuser seriously thinks she has had enough and is ready to quit, she has already taken the first step in redeeming herself. A significant goal of sobriety is redemption, but just like all things recovery-related, it's not easy to obtain. To get to this point, an addict will need your help to recognize that she has a problem abstaining from her DOC. She will also need your help in making amends for her "wrongs." Understand that she cannot get to this point alone.

Most addicts are inherently *good* people. It is their issues with substance abuse that play a key role in their actions and words. This isn't an excuse, just a fact. None of the thousands of people I've encountered with SUDs have been happy about having it, and none of them have been pleased about the stigma attached to it. In fact, in most cases, it takes many long and frustrating years before an addict concludes that she has two choices - abstinence or death. But, even at that stage, most addicts need help maintaining their sobriety.

Honestly, trying to redeem oneself after years of taking advantage of others is like the "Boy Who Cried Wolf" story. We tell so many lies, and we manipulate so many people that no one really believes us when we actually get serious about getting "clean." So, at this point, you have two options - drive your addicted loved one's passion for being redeemed or give her a reason to relapse, returning to her "old ways." Your motivation is of the utmost importance during this step. Your goal should be to help her regain something she lost after taking that first "hit" or sip = control.

The Keys to Redemption

1. Regaining Control

When an addict regains control of his life, it is both empowering and redeeming. The drug is no longer in the driver's seat. The addict's potential (the drugs and alcohol marred) is now becoming visible. He notices this, but when others notice, redemption feels that much more real.

"Sober living" has replaced his craving to get "high." The selfishness of "use and abuse" has given way to a newfound consideration of others. He has acquired new self-respect. Thus, being in control of one's life is redeeming in itself.

2. Maintaining Control

As I said before, **the disease of addiction is a chronic, devious bitch just waiting for you to slip-**

up. Like other chronic diseases treated with daily medications, therapy, and support, addiction is no different.

The goal of this treatment is not only to get your loved one sober and "clean," but to keep her sober and "clean" indefinitely. But, staying "clean" will require daily reminders and reality checks. You, as the "helper," along with the addict, **must** be vigilant.

The truth is there are more routes to redemption than highways in all of New York, so that's a lot of roads that can be taken. Who doesn't want to redeem herself, addict or not, from past "wrongs?" Understand that we, addicts, don't go around bragging about our disease or the things it led us to do. **FYI**: If an addict goes around bragging, she is not ready for sobriety.

The "Needs"

- ❖ Treatment
- ❖ Peer Support & Recovery Coaching
- ❖ The Grieving Process

Sobriety-related *wants,* combined with the *needs* of the substance abuser, complete the "sober process." The goal of this process is to get addicts to *want* to engage in "sober living," but just like many other things in life, it will not work if specific *needs* aren't met.

1. Treatment

There are not enough words to describe how necessary treatment is to a substance abuser. It's not the most critical part of the "sober process," but it's still essential because a person can't become sober without some form of treatment. This part of the process is the very definition of *need* = required, necessary, and vital.

Like many addictions that exist, there are just as many corresponding treatments available - from detox to inpatient facilities, outpatient centers, and aftercare services. These facilities are important because treatment is the foundation of sobriety.

Most addicts go through several different stints in treatment before their consequences cause a "Turning Point" in their lives. By this time, you do not have to beg your loved one to stay in treatment – he already understands that the situation is as dire as a heart attack, and he *needs* help asap. This is usually around the time when an addict enters the "Advanced" and "End" phases of addiction. This is also when a medically monitored medication-assisted treatment (MAT) is most needed.

Substance abuse treatment helps those with substance use disorders attain homeostasis. This term refers to long-term recovery with full mind and body wellness. Its goal is to create a healthy balance in the body, which is the overall goal of sobriety.

2. Peer Support & Recovery Coaching

People often say that a doctor does not have to have had a broken leg to treat one. That may be true when treating bones; however, it's not 100% true for addiction. Honestly, a doctor, counselor, or therapist who has never suffered from addiction is at a disadvantage when trying to treat those with this disease.

But, unlike a broken leg or diabetes, there is no one right way to treat addiction. To treat addiction, one **must** know what makes an addict "tick." Who are the best people to know these things? Those that have fought and conquered this disease, people we call "our peers."

Generally, substance abuse treatment is performed by trained mental health and addiction specialists, but parts of treatment can be supplemented with "trained peers." Peer specialists are those who once suffered from substance abuse, addiction, or mental health conditions. They use their experiences to help others get "clean." Studies have shown that "peer support" increases the odds that an addict will achieve and maintain sobriety.

Study results also suggest that a peer-supported community program, focused on self-determination, can have a significant positive impact on substance addiction recovery (Boisvert, 2008).[16] Researchers of this study also found that

16. Boisvert, R. A., Martin, L. M., Grosek, M., & Clarie, A. J. (2008). Effectiveness of a peer-support community in addiction recovery: participation as intervention. Occup. Ther. Int., 15, 205–220. Retrieved from doi:10.1002/oti.257

relapse rates significantly decline when peers are included in the treatment program.

But, using "peer support" in addiction treatment was not always viewed as a viable option. The mere idea of it was considered insane in the past, but not anymore. Back then, who would have thought that one addict could actually help another one achieve sobriety? A recoveree (a recovered addict) knows what it's like to battle through triggers and cravings. He also knows what it feels like to try to redeem himself after years of "racking-up" "addiction debt."

Moreover, peers teach newly recovered addicts "sober living" habits, relapse prevention, community inclusion, sustained recovery, and how to successfully live longer and healthier lives. The reason why peers are so beneficial during the "sober process" is that they can help the recoveree establish coping skills to life without substances of abuse.

3. **The Grieving Process**

When a substance abuser enters into sobriety, she goes through a "grieving process." Why? Because her previous life, as an addict, is now gone. Before sobriety, her "addict identity" was connected and controlled by her DOC. So, taking the "substance" away from a substance abuser causes not only physical and psychological withdrawals but also an emotional withdrawal.

Remember, addicts depend on alcohol and drugs to function, so when they enter the "sober process," they are forced to live without them. Keep in mind that these "substances" were more beloved than their own family members. So, it's only right that an addict is allowed to mourn the loss of the "substances" they once held so dear.

There is a wide range of emotions involved in the "grieving process." In fact, these emotions typically fall into different stages. According to Dr. Elizabeth Kübler-Ross, a renowned psychiatrist, there are "five stages of grief." These stages include denial, anger, bargaining, depression, and acceptance. (Kübler-Ross, 1969).[17]

1. Denial: A recoveree *still* may not believe she has a problem. She may also experience "back-sliding" thoughts and words. In other words, the idea of never "using and abusing" again may upset her.

You can encourage your addicted loved one to continue treatment or maintain sobriety by helping her remember how she got to this point in her life – whenever she experiences doubts about giving up drugs or alcohol. This is also an excellent time to highlight any discrepancies between her words and actions.

2. Anger: Some recoverees are angry. Maybe, this anger is irritability because they no longer have access to drugs or alcohol...Maybe, this anger stems from a feeling of

---

17. Kübler-Ross, E. (1969). On death and dying. New York: Macmillan Publishing Company.

being pressured to give up something that made them feel good...

But honestly, the reason doesn't matter. If your addicted loved one *needs* to vent - let her vent because the anger will eventually pass.

3. Bargaining: During this stage of the "grieving process," an addict will try to strike up a deal with herself or others. For instance, an addict will tell her loved ones that she will reduce her alcohol and drug use if she doesn't have to go to treatment. And, a recovering addict will bargain with the treatment staff by saying, "I will stop doing drugs and alcohol if you give me something less potent to take in its place." The truth is this type of bargaining never works.

4. Depression: A recoveree may develop depression (i.e., hopelessness and sadness), as the treatment continues, or after he becomes 100% sober. Why? Because his DOC helped improve his mood, and now it is gone.

With his DOC now absent, there is nothing to mask the chemical imbalances in his brain, especially in the part responsible for mood. In this case, medication may be needed to help restore the balance in the brain; however, it's important to reassure your addicted loved one that life without drugs and/or alcohol will get better. This too will pass.

5. Acceptance: Accepting the loss of the DOC is the final grieving stage. This is when an addict admits he has a problem, takes steps to fix the problem, accepts that the problem is ongoing, and realizes the need for continued treatment. Acceptance is a form of giving in and letting go of the internal conflict. It is also when a recoveree acknowledges the addiction but doesn't let it control his life.

The grieving process helps an addict or recoveree "let go and move on," so allow your addicted loved one to mourn the loss of his DOC. He may miss his drug of choice, and that's ok. To help with this process, you may want to create a mock funeral for the loss of his previous life.

Fake funerals may sound silly, but it is a decent way for your loved one to grieve his prior way of living. It gives your loved one closure, which is what he needs to move on with his life. So, stage a mock funeral for his past drug abuse, complete with a eulogy.

DC Hyden's 3Ds of "Cold Turkey"

❖ Detox
❖ Detach
❖ Declare

The "sober process" increases an addict's chances of going "cold turkey." When an addict's *wants* and *needs* are met, quitting anything, from nicotine to cocaine, is a little bit easier. What is going, "cold turkey?" Well, going "cold turkey" means abruptly stopping the "use and abuse" of addictive substances.

It's a simple method, but hard to execute, and possibly dangerous, depending on what you're trying to quit. Some things can be abruptly stopped, while others must be tapered-off. The aforementioned is partially why relapse rates are higher for some drugs than others and why there are two different types of going "cold turkey."

There is an "original" and "extra cold" version of going "cold turkey." The "original" version involves "bare-knuckle stopping" the first time around. The "extra cold" version involves repeated attempts to go "cold turkey." This version builds on the required skills after each failed attempt. I believe the "extra cold" version is how most addicts stumble into quitting. Regardless if it's the "original" or "extra cold" version, there are three factors that boost the success of quitting drugs and alcohol. I call them - DC Hyden's 3Ds of "Cold Turkey."

1. Detox: This person is trying to quit the unwanted substance or "thing" he is addicted to. It's the first step and the foundation of going "cold turkey." Nicotine, alcohol, opiates, THC, caffeine, gambling, and even the wrong people need to be detoxed from an addict's system to "get sober."

It all starts with deciding to stop, taking action to stop, and then detoxing your body. Detox is about cleansing or eliminating the body of addictive substances. With most drugs, a person can do it by himself or in a detox center for alcohol and benzodiazepines. The addict is creating a clean slate, which mentally and physically prepares him for the next step.

2. Detach: In this step, the addict removes any triggers attached to the thing(s) he is trying to quit from his life. This may mean detaching from certain people, places, or things, and/or television, social media, a stressful job, or any reminders of his addiction.

What I just mentioned can be referred to as physical and mental detachment. The distance required here may sound simple, but it is difficult to execute. If possible, a great way for an addict to detach is in an inpatient treatment program, because the detox is already included. If the addict can't physically detach, then maybe he can mentally detach through meditation and exercise. Moreover, an addict may be able to detach with the help of a support group.

3. Declare: An addict who is trying to quit **must** make a declaration to herself and anyone else that is important to her. This declaration should let everyone know she is going "cold turkey" to stop "using and abusing." In other words, it should be a public yet personal promise – one she holds herself to. The hope is when she makes this declaration to others, it will add-on the pressure to keep it up.

However, the addict needs to make this declaration to someone she knows that she cannot let down (i.e., Higher

Power, child, mom/dad, girlfriend/boyfriend, or even the judge in her court case). The purpose of making this declaration is to strengthen her resolve about going "cold turkey" and to reinforce this mentality through her actions.

It Ain't Over Till It's Over

Sobriety is a culture shock to the addict-turned-recoveree.

It doesn't matter if she reached sobriety through multiple "cold turkey" attempts or just one, she *still* has to change *almost* everything in her life, so it's compatible with her new "clean" and "sober lifestyle." Welcome to the "Remission Phase" of addiction, where the drug and alcohol "use" stops, and real living begins. It is also where a recoveree has to deal with stress - without having a "substance" to use as a "crutch." But, it's essential to understand that the war on her "addict identity" and DOC ain't over.

Actually, the battle is just now heating up. Remission takes hard work, dedication, discipline, and lots of help to maintain it. The good news is you, as her "helper," can play an imperative role in her remission. You can help her get her *wants* and *needs* met.

How? Well, the simple act of forgiving an addict or recoveree is almost as *freeing* as walking out of a county lock-up. This feeling of being *free* can motivate recoveree to make amends for past mistakes – if it is applied correctly.

Making atonement by repaying "addiction debt" and fixing something that was broken is redeeming for a recoveree. Redemption comes in the form of regained self-respect, self-worth, self-direction, and just peace of mind; this is the start of the "sober process."

The next step is professional addiction treatment services that involve peer support recovery coaching. The "grieving process" is another part of the "sober process." The purpose of the "grieving process" is to help the recoveree move on from the loss of her drug of choice. So, encourage your addicted loved one by forgiving her and allowing her to grieve her former life. If there is ever a time she needs your support, it's now, when she is taking steps towards recovery.

Go with her to treatment appointments - without complaining, be present, active, and show a genuine interest throughout the treatment process. **FYI**: *A little encouragement goes a long way.*

Keep in mind that the end goal for both you and your addicted loved one is complete sobriety. Sometimes, sobriety is a requirement for an addict to regain something he lost, like access to his children or partner/spouse or even his freedom. Judges often order an addict into treatment and then require complete sobriety as a condition for continued freedom, visitation with his children, etc.

> ## - ADDICT INSIGHT -
> ### "SOBRIETY IS NOT DIFFICULT; IT'S THE GETTING TO SOBRIETY PART THAT KILLS THE ADDICT."

Well, you can use that same tactic with your addicted loved one. In other words, you can use sobriety, as a condition in a relationship with you.

You have the power to order sober requirements for any situation – i.e., to continue the marriage, to see his children, to get financial support, or even to remain friends. After all of the misery that took place to get to the point of being "clean" and sober, requirements should be absolute.

To gain and maintain the desired change, black-and-white conditions **must** be outlined.

Setting forth these conditions is where honesty and transparency come into play. The addict in recovery does not want to return to a life of addiction and all the shit by-product it produces. So, say this to your addicted loved one, "If you really want (fill-in-the-blank), then you **must** remain sober." It's as simple as that. You don't even have to explain why you are giving her the ultimatum.

You can also use a wide variety of technological or traditional methods (requirements) to hold her accountable for her actions. For instance, it is common to have an ignition interlock device installed in the car, truck, or motorcycle of an addict to hold her accountable for her actions.

So, if she stops at a liquor store on the way home, her loved ones will know and hold her accountable for going against her oath to stay sober. The great thing about this method is that it also alerts the addict's loved ones when she fails an alcohol test. Alcohol detection ankle bracelets and mobile phone breathalyzers also help keep alcoholics in- check. Even your local drug store has drug screens you can buy for your addicted loved one. The good thing about these drug screens is you can use them on your addicted loved one at any time. All these suggestions allow you to play an active role in your loved one's sobriety. Do not be scared to use sober requirements to keep her "clean." And don't be shy about holding her accountable. The truth is, if someone had used these methods on me, my road to sobriety would have been shorter and smoother. Sobriety is not difficult; it's the getting to sobriety that kills the addict – literally.

Achieving sobriety is not the end of the road. No, it is just the beginning. It's a new beginning for the recoveree. The new sober and "clean" life is filled with all kinds of "teachable moments" - for the recoveree and his "helpers." The recoveree has a lot of loss time to make-up for.

Since his addiction has stunted his growth, he now has to function like he's not already behind the eight-ball. During this time, the recoveree's "helpers" learn how an adult can actually mature right before their very eyes. But both the "helpers" and the recoveree will have their patience tested in the process.

However, the most important thing is that the recoveree accepts sobriety and the control over his life that comes with it. Sobriety is magnificent, but there is always the threat of relapse when you are inflicted with the disease of addiction.

CHAPTER 10

Relapse

I'm a chronic "relapser." I guess I always will be.
— Cory Haim, actor
1971 - 2010
(Cause of Death: *Pneumonia with Eight Different Prescription Medications in His System*)

You Spin Me Round

I never considered my return to drinking after having sober periods, relapses. In my mind, a relapse consisted of being committed to stopping, and then relapsing, as a result of an uncontrolled break in a sobriety commitment. In my case, I was never fully committed to being sober, so in my mind, I never really relapsed.

The fact that I couldn't see that I relapsed and did so with the frequency of a hooker working on a busy Saturday night was a real deterrent to my sobriety. The definition of relapse is falling back into former habits — i.e., returning to drug use after a period of abstinence. Clinically, relapse is defined as the reappearance of addiction and its accompanying symptoms. For a recoveree, it's a lapse in the "Remission Phase," in which continued use could put her back in the "End Phase" of addiction. Ultimately, it is a reoccurrence of the conflict between a person and her addicted self. For an addict, relapse is losing a battle in an ongoing war, and it **must** be recognized as just that - a lost battle, but not the end of the war. *Relapse is an opportunity for honest reflection on one's loss of control. It is also the time to ask if one is truly ready to quit their addictive habit.*

I was dishonest for years, lying about my sobriety, trying to fake being on the "straight-and-narrow," but all the while thinking about how I was going to get my next "fix." The only time I truly honestly stopped drinking was when I was in jail or to appease the program guidelines I had to abide by to get my license back. I went from "Pre-contemplation" to the "Action" Stage of Change. From knowing I had to quit, to quitting, but not putting in the necessary work to sustain the quit.

There were mornings where I cursed my drug of choice. This DOC hate usually occurred after I learned all of the degenerate things I had done the night before – things I had forgotten. There were also afternoons I swore I would never drink again because of my throbbing headache, stomach-churning nausea, and blood spit-up. Moreover, there were nights that if my addiction were a person, I would have beat him to a bloody pulp because I blamed it for causing me to crash my motorcycle *and* my muscle car, the car I invested a lot of my time and money into restoring.

My addiction spun me around, and it was an awful ride that I paid damn good money for. The only time I even thought about stopping was when the consequences hurt my pockets or body, thus began my cycle of stopping and restarting. I became depressed because I didn't have control over my life like I thought I did. During this time, I would build my body and finances back up. Once I was stable, I became cocky and my "addict identity" took over the driver's seat. At this point, the truth was that I just did not care... until I got into a bad situation again. Then, the cycle repeated.

I couldn't see the big picture. If I could have, I would have realized that I was unceremoniously caught up in the rinse cycle of a washing machine. I was going round-n-round through the motions, but not getting "clean" in the end. I was not ready. Part of me didn't want to give it up. Part of me saw no good reason to

---

- ADDICT INSIGHT -

"ADDICTS DON'T NEED A REASON TO "USE" BECAUSE THEY "USE" REGARDLESS OF THE REASON."

---

stop. It was my inability to understand the reason why I relapsing that kept me in the cycle. Understanding the reasons behind relapses help provide all parties with a better grasp on how to prevent them from happening.

Addicts don't need a reason to "use" because they "use" regardless of the reason. After each damaging episode, part of me *wanted* to stop my "use and abuse." In my mind, I would stop when I was good and ready to stop. And, when I felt ready, I quit my "use" - for short periods - until I forgot. The problem, at least partially, with my SUD, is that it seemed to accompany a loss in short-term memory. My intoxicated episodes were extremely traumatizing and debilitating to all of my loved ones; however, the "fall out" from these episodes never lasted long enough to make me *want* to change my behavior.

Do you remember the studies I cited earlier that suggested that bad memories have a greater effect than the good ones? Well, those who suffer from the disease of addiction have volume upon volume of bad memories, cataloged like books in the library. Those bad memories impact us differently. **So, by now, it's clear that the mind of a person with a SUD is *abnormal*. It's important to understand that human reasoning is based on memories. More specifically, learned experiences, good or bad, shape our views and actions, and eventually,**

our outcomes. Learned experiences also shape our reasoning, and our reasoning shapes our realities.

So, why do some addicts relapse? You can count the number of hairs on your head, multiply that by 10, and you'll still only get a fraction of the possible reasons why some addicts relapse. My experiences, as an addict and later as a counselor to other addicts, has given me enough insight to place "Relapse Reasons" or (RRs) into two categories - internal and external. The internal reasons are usually based on inner conflicts and "disturbances" of the mind, body, and/or soul. And, the external reasons are typically based on environmental factors or events that trigger addicts into doing things they shouldn't – like sampling with their DOCs after getting "clean."

The Internal Reasons

1. **H.A.L.T**

H.A.L.T. or "Hungry, Angry, Lonely, and Tired" is an internal cause of relapses. These factors may seem small and innocent, but they can quickly cause an addict to return to his former drug or alcohol habit. H.A.L.T. takes an addict out of his comfort zone, possibly triggering a relapse.

While non-addicted people can effectively work on an empty stomach (hungry) with a disgruntled boss on their backs (angry), go home to an empty home (lonely) at the end of the day, and fall fast asleep once their heads hit their pillows (tired) – it doesn't quite work the same for recoverees. In fact, for a recoveree, these factors may cause a light to turn on, triggering their "use and abuse" behaviors.

2. Pressure, Stress & Anxiety

The recoveree faces increased stress, anxiety, and pressures, just from being "clean" and sober. She no longer has her 'go-to' crutch - the crutch that once served as a saving grace for her. Once she chose sobriety, she had to cope with reality - without getting "high." Life is not always easy, but add-in the pressure a recoveree puts on herself to maintain her sobriety, and you've got a recipe for stress with anxiety as a side order. Recoverees typically experience an "elephant in spandex type of pressure" – one that stems from unrealistically high expectations that have been placed on them by themselves and others. During recovery, we addicts strove to atone, be forgiven, and be redeemed, but living-up to unrealistically high expectations can lead to an epic relapse.

3. Self-Hurt/Self-Harm

Some people are addicted to tattoos, while for others, it may be S&M... However, for an addict, it's his drug of choice. Psychiatrists, who are smarter and more expensive than me, will tell you that one of the reasons people abuse "substances" is to punish themselves. As a self-destructive "Professional Addict" with years of experience under my belt, I can confirm this theory. We, addicts, live in a perpetual state of self-harm. In other words, subconsciously or consciously, some addicts "abuse" drugs or alcohol as a way to hurt themselves. Self-punishment for unresolved emotions (i.e., guilt, shame, etc.) keep the cycle of addiction going.

We *want* to punish ourselves for the emotional, physical, or financial pain we put others through. Even during sobriety and recovery from drugs, that guilt is *still* there, because many of our offenses have long-term effects. So, we inflict pain on ourselves to mimic the heartache and pain we inflicted on others. **Understand that self-mutilation is as much a part of the addiction as dishonesty, manipulation, wasted potential, and financial ruin.**

If addiction is a slow form of suicide, leading to the end, self-injury is the foreplay, starting things off. It's not intended to be lethal; we just cause ourselves enough pain to not make us feel so bad, even if we're unaware we are doing it. Because substance abuse and addiction are often viewed as major causes of concern, sometimes addicts speed into recovery, leaving the underlying cause(s) of the self-harm unresolved. Remember, to experience long-lasting recovery, an addict or recoveree must find the answers to internal questions like "Why do I harm myself?"

The Internal Answer is...

The key to preventing relapses is to effectively handle each emotion as it occurs. It's a fact that H.A.L.T is going to happen. Pressure, stress, and anxiety are natural parts of life. In other words, it's a part of living in a world with other people. As you know guilt and shame are difficult emotions, however, they should not make you *want* to hurt yourself with your drug of choice. Still, the outcome of these emotions will depend on how the recoveree decides to deal with them.

Remember the chapter on "To Enable is to Kill?" - the one where I taught you the acronym A.R.M. = Accept, Redirect, and Motivate? Well, this method can also be applied here. It's a good tactic for friends and family, who are desperately trying to prevent a loved one's relapse.

It is also beneficial for recoveree, who is desperately trying not to relapse. But, to prevent this from happening, a recoveree **must** accept that a current H.A.L.T. feeling or emotion will take or is taking him out of his comfort zone. Your goal, at this point, is to redirect his attention towards something he can control. It is also important that you give him something to focus on, so he's not obsessing over his DOC. The aim is for the recoveree to motivate himself to stay "clean" even with H.A.L.T. factors at-play.

And, although the A.R.M. method can be performed alone, it is probably best to be assisted by a trained psychologist or therapist. This mental health professional can help the recoveree process his emotions. **FYI**: Psychologists and therapists can be expensive; however, recoverees can access more income-based counseling services through non-profit organizations. Professional help can give a recoveree or their helper, an outside perspective and find a realistic resolution to any issues he is facing.

During recovery, once the cycle has stopped, there needs to be resolution through learned coping skills. Although many eventually make it to the *promised land* of recovery, they need to understand that prolonged recovery is not *promised*. The truth is many recoverees relapse because they lack the coping skills required to live everyday life. If they are unable, for some reason, to atone for past "wrongs," or automatically prosper, they punish themselves for it by picking up their DOC.

The External

1. People, Places, and Things

If you have dealt with someone who is trying to get "clean" from addiction, I'm sure you've heard the term, "people, places, and things." It's a widely used adage to describe things that can get an addict in trouble. This is another one of those "simple ideas," but complicated tasks to execute.

Often people (i.e., "enablers," dealers, and "stress-makers") are in places (i.e., homes, neighborhoods, schools/work), where things (triggers) get mixed into a lethal addiction/relapse cocktail.

Remember in that kid's movie, where the lions talked about the "The Circle of Life?" Well, "people, places and things" can be "The Circle of Death" for addicts and recoverees alike. The beginning of addiction, its driving force, and possibly the ending of the addiction cycle is interconnected through "people, place, and things."

2. Triggers

Triggers are "external events" that can produce very uncomfortable emotional or psychiatric symptoms, such as anxiety, panic, discouragement, despair, and/or negative self-talk" (SAMHSA: Action Planning for Prevention and Recovery).[18] Keep in mind that triggers can be damn near anything. They could be hiding on the street corner, where the recoveree would "cop dope." The smell of cigarette smoke could be a trigger for a person who would smoke a 12-pack of cigarettes a day. A trigger could also be a trip to the convenience store in which a recoveree with a gambling problem would frequent to purchase hundreds of scratch-off lotto tickets. Or a trigger could be making a trip to the part of town a sex addict recoveree would go to pick-up prostitutes.

A trigger is an association with someone or something. In the case of an addict or recoveree, it is an event or cir-

---

18. SAMSHA (2003). Action planning for prevention and recovery. Retrieved from http://www.npaihb.org/wp-content/uploads/2018/12/action-planning-for-recovery.

cumstance that somehow becomes associated with drug and alcohol "use and abuse." Generally, it's only the 'good' parts of "using and abusing" that are tied to the trigger. In other words, positive drug or alcohol associations get linked to euphoria, excitement, numbness, or just comfort.

Negative associations can also be tied to drug and alcohol habits; however, these don't elicit the same strong responses as negative memories. An example of a positive association trigger would be a recoveree craving an ice-cold can of beer or two or three on a summer's day because he would drink on hot days. On the flip side, a negative association trigger would be an urge to get drunk or "high" on the day a loved one died, as an "escape from reality" mechanism. These event dates (i.e., tragedies, anniversaries of death, etc.) are called "trigger events."

Triggers trigger cravings.

A drug craving is like a food craving or any other type of craving on steroids. My definition of a craving is a short-lived urge to "use" a specific drug or drink a specific alcoholic beverage. This desire is triggered in one's subconscious but presents itself through various internal and external cues. For instance, let us say a biker is walking and sees another biker riding a motorcycle down the road on a nice day. He may really want to ride based simply on the sound and sight of another person's joy ride. This biker is experiencing an urge – a desire. He craves that motorcycle ride like addicts and recoverees crave drugs and alcohol. It is this craving that is a tipping point for relapses.

The External Answer is...

We have just as much control over our environments as we do over our emotions. Therefore, what we can't control should not dictate the emotions we can control over. Awareness and vigilance are **musts** for recoverees and their loved ones. Recoverees, especially, **must** be aware of their surroundings and how those surroundings are impacting them. "Helpers" **must** also be vigilant, so recoverees understand the vital role their environments play in their sobriety.

Regardless of the "people, places, or things" that can trigger cravings, the following steps may help prevent relapses:

1.   R&R - Recognize & Realize

Being able to *recognize* triggers and *realizing* how they impact our lives is the ultimate goal of R&R. A recoveree **must** be aware and almost ultra-sensitive in *recognizing* what could be triggering his cravings. The best way to stay ahead of triggers is to determine the where, when, why, how, and what is sparking the trigger. R&R also involves *recognizing* the trouble ahead. For instance, when you see the flashing lights of a police car that is parked on the side of a road, and you slow down to go unnoticed. You realize that the cop could give you a ticket if you are going too fast, so you proceed with caution. The same idea, of proceeding with caution, should be implemented for the recoveree.

Along with identifying and being aware of the trigger, it is also crucial to be self-aware. Help the recoveree become more self-aware by observing and documenting whatever causes behavioral changes in response to triggers and cravings. Help her catalog and categorize the triggers so that she can avoid or work through them. I always reassure my clients that they are **not** crazy if talking things through to themselves gives them comfort.

The thing is, talking to themselves helps with R&R because it provides recoverees with a chance to reflect on the triggers and their impact. So, talk it out and talk it through with your loved one, who is recovering from addiction or who has already obtained sobriety.

2. Constant Reminder – Constant Deterrent

Having this mindset can be a *saving grace* for recoverees and their "helpers." If addiction is a lifelong illness, then recovery is constant reminders and constant deterrents. Both serve as daily doses of medicine. There are many ways for the recoveree to remind himself not to go to trigger-worthy places or hang around with trigger-worthy people. These reminders and deterrents help him avoid falling back into old habits and routines.

Souvenirs (consequences) of active addictions serve as great reminders of what not to do. Examples of this are keeping receipts that show how much money your loved one lost to "addiction debt," jail/prison identifications, or "keepsakes" and pictures of her lying in hospital beds. A recoveree should also have positive reminders around her – ones that highlight a "clean," sober life. More specifically, surround your loved one with the awards and acknowledgments she gained during treatment. These "tokens" will remind her of the control she gained through sobriety. Don't forget to shuffle the items around, because a recoveree's eyes will get used to seeing the same things in the same spots – even if they are awards and acknowledgments, so change them around from time-to-time to keep things "fresh."

By using R&R and documenting triggers, recoverees are better able to identify and avoid triggers. R&R can prevent RRs. "Helpers" should know these triggers and constantly remind and deter recoverees from returning to bad habits. At this stage, niceties and formalities should be pushed aside, just like in the "Phases of Addiction."

Once again, don't be afraid that you're nagging him because being subtle will not deter him much. Rather, constantly remind him of his triggers and deter him by warning him that these cravings could cause him to lose *everything* – again. So, **at this point, the goal is to constantly remind recoverees about the seriousness of their**

**disease by keeping the consequences of their previ-
ous drug or alcohol habits at the forefronts of their
minds**. The hope is that this will deter any impending relapses.

A Case of the F#%k Its!

We all have one those days where we just want to put our
middle fingers up to the world. These are the days where the
external around us and the internal inside us bring nothing
but conflict from every angle. This type of day, we just want
to say "F#%k It!" and give up. Well, this attitude is common
amongst addicts and recoverees. It is also a common reason
these individuals give for relapsing.

It is this defeatist attitude that keeps addicts trapped
in a cycle of addiction. This "woe is me," "the world is out
to get me, and things won't get better" mindset has led to
many relapses. So, how addicts and recoverees combat this
common way of thinking and feeling?

The key is to "adapt." Humans **must** adapt to survive,
while recoverees **must** adapt to remain sober. Sobriety is a
new way of life; it's a new way of living and thinking. The
defeatist addict attitude needs to be run over and left in the
rearview mirror. It's hard for an addict to adapt to tough
times, so she uses her drug of choice as a getaway instead.
Thus, a recoveree has to master adaption for every disap-
pointing or rough situation. At this stage, adaption skills

are learned behaviors, so recovery professionals and sober family members are the best teachers.

I teach recoverees life skills like coping techniques, stress relievers, and even how to ride motorcycles, all as healthier forms of "escape." Some of my most important lessons have involved avoiding tunnel vision and looking at the bigger picture. Tunnel vision is a singular focus on the here-and-now. But, as part of a recoveree's support system, you **must** be a constant reminder that the here-and-now is not a permanent situation. Let her know that everyone has bad days, tough times, and dry spells, then tell her about yours and how you dealt with them.

Another example is a "fresh-out of-jail" parolee. I know more than a few guys who have had a hard time adapting to life outside of prison. They aren't used to having a "normal" life. After spending years in an institution, they finally become *free* only to have the usual frustrations of everyday life become too much for them to deal with. Either consciously or subconsciously, they find ways to "mess-up," so bad that it leads them right back to addiction, homelessness, and jail or prison.

We are the sum of the decisions we make. Unfortunately, however, for addicts, this disease leads to more bad decisions than good. These impulsive and clouded decisions come back to haunt them, even once they become sober.

If there was anything that gave me a thought of "F#%k It, I should just go back to using," it was the continual repercussions of the decisions I made while intoxicated. The feeling was like having every ounce of my breath knocked out of me, after falling off a motorcycle, doing 50 mph. It was as frustrating as hell. I thought I was doing all the right things, but I was *still* paying for all the dumb-ass mistakes I made years ago.

Bad decisions get compounded with bad decisions, and then interest gets added to that, leading to a mountain of trouble. This is just another added layer of frustrations; a recoveree **must** learn to handle. So, the most pressing thing you need to get across to your loved one is that he needs to understand that shit happens, and it's normal to be stressed out about it. But, regardless of what life throws at him, he can't lose sight of the big picture = a healthy and prosperous "sober life." It doesn't matter what he is currently going through; his focus should remain on the big picture.

In other words, when bad things happen, he needs to be able to shift from the tunnel vision of the present to the importance of the larger picture in the future. Again, it's all about dealing with life without being under the influence of alcohol and/or drugs. Help your loved one understand that trouble usually doesn't last and remind him that he is one of the most resilient people you've ever met. Therefore, both recoverees and their "helpers" should hold this military saying close to their hearts, "Suck It Up and Drive On!"

Prepare for the Worst, But Expect the Best

After all of the heartache and pain, the addict has finally become sober and "clean." Now what? There's no going back, because, at this point, all involved parties should know the "addict identity" is waiting for the recoveree to return to "old habits." So, the best thing you can do for yourself, as a "helper" is to prepare for the worst (a relapse), but concentrate on the newly acquired control your loved one has gained through sobriety. The strength of sobriety lies not only in the control a recoveree has gained but also in her self-expectation of a better life. I try not to think about relapsing because those thoughts could take me somewhere I don't want to be. So, I avoid relapses by knowing exactly what I have to do and then doing it.

Here's how I apply what I teach to others:

I know when I am feeling H.A.L.T., I need to take a time-out if time permits. Then, once I am feeling more in control, I remedy the situation. If a time-out is not possible, then I take a step back and re-assess how I can prevent these feelings from taking me places I don't want to go. Pressure, stress, and anxiety are the inconvenient parts of my life, so I A.R.M. myself = meaning I accept the unwanted feelings, redirect my emotions and energy, and then turn them into motivation for the big picture. I know that if certain emotions like guilt or shame are left unprocessed and not handled properly, a relapse may occur, leading to my "use and abuse" patterns returning. *So, I suck it up and drive on.*

I know that I can't be around certain "people, places, and things." I had close friends that drank and smoked while "enabling" me every step of the way. Since I stopped *wanting* to drink and smoke, some of those friends stopped coming around, as well. I don't go to bars unless I *want* to drink, and because I don't *want* to drink anymore, I stay far away from bars.

I use R&R to prevent me from using alcohol as a crutch. I **recognize** which people, places, and things I need to avoid because of what they have done to me in the past. I **realize** precisely how they helped keep me in a cycle of addiction. I also rely on constant reminders and constant deterrents to keep me on the straight-and-narrow. Sometimes, however, I miss those "people, places, and things," but oh well – *I still suck it up and drive on.*

I know my triggers and what's going to give me cravings. With R&R, I **recognize** what those triggers are, and I **realize** the potential for relapse. When I'm around a trigger or experience a craving, I proceed with caution. R&R keeps me aware of what is happening within me and around me. I also share what triggers me with my closet friends, so they, too, can constantly remind and deter me from "using and abusing" again. The people and things in my environment are my constant reminders, while also serving as constant deterrents. I *still* get cravings, but my control of my "sober life" is more potent than any craving, so *I suck it up and drive on.*

Some say relapse is a natural part of sobriety, like the fall a child may take, as he learns to walk. I don't buy this train of thought. A relapse is a failure. In life, we never plan to fail, but failing to plan is the perfect way to return to addiction. In any good relapse prevention plan, acknowledgment is an especially important step. During this step, a recoveree acknowledges that a relapse is possible, but it doesn't have to be a guarantee. Recoverees also acknowledge how H.A.L.T. emotions or "people, places, and things" can trigger cravings. That is why recoverees should prepare themselves for battle. In other words, they should prepare themselves for the "upsets" and "downturns" that will surely come. But they should also *still* expect the best out of this new life that they now control.

At first, it may seem like your brain has too much to look out for and too much to be vigilant about. Well, the adaptation will naturally happen if the recoveree and his

---

- ADDICT INSIGHT -

"STRESSING ABOUT A RELAPSE HAPPENING ONLY LEADS TO A RELEASE HAPPENING."

"helpers" continue to fight. Sure, there are family, work, bills, and romantic relationships to consider, but these are not the main things recoverees should be worried about. First and foremost, recoverees should focus on themselves because self-focus = self-preservation.

This can be accomplished by helping your loved one become self-aware of the following:

1. The internal causes of relapses are simplistic. They involve both biological and emotional factors.

2. The external causes of relapses involve things that are outside of ourselves – i.e., environment.

3. You are in control of how you handle the "Relapse Reasons" (RRs).

4. How you handle each reason is the strongest indicator of if you'll relapse or not.

Stressing about a relapse happening only leads to a relapse happening. So, don't allow your loved one to focus on relapsing. However, if it happens, it's not the end of the world. A recoveree can return to the "Remission Phase." A recoveree and his "helpers" **must** work together to discover what he was thinking, feeling, and doing right before the relapse. The recoveree **must** also make the necessary changes (i.e., adjusted treatment plans, goals, more supervision, etc.). Tell your loved one, "Don't make relapse prevention harder than it has to be." Moreover, you and the recoveree **must** learn together. In other words, figure out what triggers his cravings and what deters them. At the same time, he **must** also learn how to live without his DOC. My last piece of advice and last acronym is K.I.S.S = "keep it simple, stupid."

A trigger = a craving = a relapse. With fewer triggers, there are fewer chances of relapsing and a greater chance of success.

CHAPTER 11

The Sober Addict

"I'm a tenacious drug addict. I give it up and I don't give it up. I put it down and I pick it up. But I'm also a tenacious "recoveree." I never quit trying to quit." [19]

— **Scott Weiland, front man of Stone Temple Pilots**

1967 - 2015

(Cause of Death: *Overdose of Cocaine, Ethanol and Methylenedioxyamphetamine-MDA)*

It Ain't Easy

You may be wondering what a "sober addict" is. It's me; it's a recoveree or anyone who has battled with a SUD and made it to the sobriety *promised land*. In other words, a "sober addict" is someone who is in recovery from addiction and has overcome his internal conflict with his "addict alter ego." As I've stated before, addiction is a lifelong disease, an

19. Weiland, S. & Ritz, D. (2011) Not dead & not for sale: A memoir. New York, NY: Simon and Schuster..

internal conflict - with no cure. So, as depressing as it may sound, a recovering addict will **never** be totally *free* from his addiction. It's just a part of himself that he will *always* have to control. It is also a part of himself that he will need to monitor. That is, he will *always* have to be aware that his addiction is lurking in the background, waiting to regain control of his life. ***The truth is being a "sober addict" ain't easy, so everyone involved must be vigilant against relapse every single day of every single month of every single year.***

Hyper-vigilance is a word that comes to mind when I think back to my "fresh-out of-jail" "cold turkey" days. I made every attempt to not tempt myself by avoiding anything alcohol or drug-related. I did everything to avoid being sucked back in, from turning off enticing television commercials to quickly looking away when I noticed discarded bottles of beer, liquor, and wine on the side of the street. These things made me feel like the world wanted me to relapse. Even in my dreams, my fear of relapse was vivid. I remember waking up feeling guilty after having nightmares, where I picked up my drug of choice again. I felt like everything I was taking in from the environment was directly or indirectly leading back to alcohol abuse. I know it was all in my head, and I was being super-sensitive, but, at the time, it frightened me enough to keep me on the straight-and-narrow.

Honestly, being sober and an addict at the same time is a balancing act. On the one hand, the recoveree is trying to navigate this new, curvy road without "liquid courage" or a "magic pill." On the other hand, he is trying to manage life with a chronic illness that is waiting for him to slip-up. Then, add in family, friends, then work obligations, and you have a ton of weight on his shoulders – all while he is either trying to recover or remain sober.

This balancing act would be difficult for any multitasker, but it is ten times worse for a recoveree, who is already behind the eight-ball. So, the best way to help your recovering or newly recovered addict balance his life is to support him. When our lives are balanced, we live better, and we tend to feel more fulfilled. It doesn't matter if we have an addiction or not; we all need equilibrium in our lives to be our best selves. *"Dealing with life on life's terms"* is a phrase we, substance abuse counselors, commonly reserve for recoverees new to sobriety and those who are "sober addicts."

Dealing with Life on Life's Terms

This phrase implies that those in recovery **must** experience and handle life - without the assistance of mind-altering "substances." What this means is that "everyday frustrations" are just that – "everyday frustrations," and should be handled as such - not with a bottle, blunt, or pill.

The tactics I provided in the *Relapse* chapter should be utilized every day to help your loved one deal with life issues as they come. Remember the following steps: (1) constantly remind, (2) constantly deter, and (3) prepare for the worst, but expect the best. The recoveree and his "helpers" **must** *still* beware – "a sober addict" is *still* a recovering addict with addictive tendencies and mindset. He is in the "Remission Phase" of addiction, but therapy to change his behavior is *still* needed because even though he is "out of the oven," he could *still* be burned by the flames of his "addict-identity."

Active Addict Vs. Inactive Addict

People label what they see, and what people see first are our behaviors. The term "addict" is often assigned to a person based on her actions. What separates active and inactive addicts is *action*. A "sober addict" is an inactive addict. She is no longer actively "using and abusing" her drug of choice.

In other words, she is no longer disappearing to "shoot up" in a back ally, fighting cops because she is "high" on PCP, or missing work because she has one hell of a hangover. Her previous behaviors no longer apply. The greatest sign that a person is a "sober addict" is her behavior. Jesus said it best, "You will know them by their fruits:" Matt 7:16. "Fruits," meaning one's actions.

- ADDICT INSIGHT -

"A "SOBER ADDICT" IS STILL AN ADDICT – EVEN IF HE DOESN'T BEHAVE LIKE ONE."

If you want to be a "sober addict," you have to change your mentality, because that is the only way you can change your actions (behaviors). So, if you are trying to help a "sober addict" get "clean," one way to do that is to encourage him to seek Cognitive Behavioral Therapy (CBT). This type of psychotherapy is short-term and to-the-point. More specifically, it focuses on the problem. CBT usually involves one-on-one counseling sessions with a therapist or counselor or self-directed online sessions.

"CBT works by changing people's attitudes and their behavior by focusing on the thoughts, images, beliefs, and attitudes that are held (a person's cognitive processes) and how these processes relate to the way a person behaves, as a way of dealing with emotional problems" (Martin, 2018).[20] The basic tenet is that if you change your thoughts, your behaviors and actions will follow. The way a person with SUD perceives himself and the events around him can perpetuate his addiction.

---

20. Martin, B. (2018). In-Depth: Cognitive behavioral therapy. Psych Central. Retrieved from https://psychcentral.com/lib/in-depth-cognitive-behavioral-therapy

For example, an active addict believes that it doesn't matter if he quits, because he is an unworthy failure. With CBT, an inactive "sober addict" learns how to have more positive thoughts, amid negative situations or events. The result? He has more positive reactions to these events.

"Once an addict, always an addict," right? Like most things in life, the answer is not a simple "Yes" or "No." Those diagnosed with a substance use disorder have a chronic condition that doesn't just disappear. With interventions like Cognitive Behavioral Therapy, peer support, and proper healthcare, the symptoms of addiction appear to lessen. But remember, a "sober addict" is *still* an addict – even if he doesn't behave like one.

Substitutions

Once a recoveree can substitute her negative thoughts, she **must** then substitute her drug of choice for something more powerful, but less destructive. If someone tells your loved one to avoid substitution tactics, kindly tell that person to F**k Off! This strategy worked for me and millions of other "sober addicts." Drugs and alcohol are so much more than just habits; rather, they are all-encompassing passions. Now, as a "sober addict," your loved one has to find something that she can be just as passionate about – something that will replace the "substance" she quit. After all, **there are soo many different forms of "high."**

I'm not talking about replacing artificial sweeteners with sugar. I mean replacing good with spectacular, replacing a tickle with an orgasm, and replacing death with life. A "sober addict" **must** find a replacement for the "substance" that gave her euphoria, even if the feeling is short-lived. The substitution has to be better. But, what's better than drugs and alcohol? I'll start with a list of the most obvious = God (Higher Power), family, health/fitness, wealth, and motorcycles!

Religion: Religion has been a driving force in nearly everything, from love to war, for as long as people have been on Earth. A Higher Power can be the ultimate motivating factor in maintaining sobriety. God, Allah, Jehovah, Buddha, regardless of what you call your Higher Power, it gives purpose and something to strive towards. A Higher Power is synonymous with "higher standards." Christianity, Islam, Catholicism, and Judaism can replace the time an addict gives to unworthy self-destructive causes. Organized religion also adds a needed social aspect to recovery, in fellowship with others, but an individualized relationship with their Higher Power can also work for recoverees. Therefore, religion is a one-stop-substitute for drugs and alcohol.

Family & Friends: Suffering from a selfish disease like addiction alienates those who care about the addict. This alienation stems from the lies, stealing, and manipulation done by the AAA to others, namely loved ones. During the addiction, addicts hurt those closest to them the most.

But, once a recoveree goes through treatment, he can replace his love for his DOC with the love he neglected to give to his family, friends, and significant other. A romantic relationship, parenting, and giving to others (volunteering) are time-consuming, but admirable substitutes for alcohol and drugs. Like with the religious substitution, a recoveree can concentrate on this instead of on drugs or alcohol.

Health: Most addicts neglect way more than just their family and friends. While they were "using," they pretty much stuck their middle fingers up at their health. Well, guess what? A desire to live a long life - one that they now have control over - is a great motivator.

A recoveree's health can also be an all-encompassing substitute like religion, family, and friends, however; this substitute is more self-centered. There aren't any "downsides" to getting fit, especially when compared to "using and abusing.

Walking, running, going to the gym, and having sex, along with almost any other physical activity performed in moderation, for at least 20-minutes, can be beneficial and life-extending for a recoveree.

Wealth: Addiction is more than just a disease of the mind and body - it also infects bank accounts, purses, and wallets like a plague, sucking them dry of any life. By the time a recoveree gets to the "Maintenance" Stage of Change, she is probably thousands-of-dollars in debt. And she also owes anyone, whoever tried to help her, but got "addiction debt" instead.

So, as the recoveree's support system, your job is not to overwhelm her with financial worries. However, you will want to tap into her motivation for a less stressful life. Money and long-term wealth = a more peaceful life. It's written that "For the love of money is the root of evil" (1 Timothy 6:10). So, a recoveree doesn't have to love money to use it as a substitute for drugs and alcohol. The truth is her sobriety/recovery won't last long without financial security or support.

Riding: Frankly, alcohol and drugs are "escapes." Substances of abuse temporarily transport an addict's mind and body away from whatever troubles he is having. We all know that this type of "ride" ain't good for the mind or body - it's fake.

So, encourage your loved one to substitute drugs and/or alcohol with a *real* ride - a ride that's good for the mind, body, and soul. Jumping on a motorcycle and going for a ride takes you away from your troubles in more ways than one, so encourage him to go for a motorcycle ride, if possible, instead of "using and abusing." Motorcycling isn't for everyone, but it doesn't hurt to ask your loved one if she'd be open to taking an exciting motorcycle ride.

Ride to Live & Live to Ride

I ride to stay sober. To make my recovery as easy as possible, I found something I could substitute for every reason I'd give for "using and abusing." I drank for many different reasons. I drank when I was lonely, bored, happy, and sad. I drank to celebrate, to mourn, to fit in, and to stand out. I drank to keep calm, to excite myself, to get sleep, and to keep myself awake. I drank to cool down in the summer and to warm up in the winter. I drank because I thought it was cool. I drank because it tasted good and made me feel even better. I drank because it was a part of me - biologically, mentally, emotionally, and socially.

But I don't drink anymore. I ride my motorcycle instead. Sobriety cleared up my way of thought processing like acne cream clears up pimples on a teenage face. You see, I changed how I perceived my drug of choice, and it changed me for better. It allowed me to substitute my destructive behaviors for constructive ones. It helped me look at everything from a different perspective. The reasons I *wanted* to "use and abuse" are the same reasons that make me now *want* to ride my motorcycle.

Riding does even more for me now than alcohol and drugs did for me then. When I'm on my bike going down the road, every ounce of me feels stimulated, excited, and calm at the same damn time. It's like tuning-out to tune-in. While my brain focuses on the road, my body reacts to the environment. It's one of the best time-outs in the world. It's an "escape" from the rest of the world.

My mind zips along at maximum speed, processing everything around me, yet I am calmed by the mighty roar of the engine. On the "twos," you see the world at a different angle, almost like looking through a different lens. However, when you are drunk and "high," you see life through beer goggles. And, honestly, it's one "messed-up" view. But when you are motorcycling, you get to see the world how it really is, up-close-and-personal, without the protection of your cage on wheels.

So, with drugs and alcohol, an addict gives up control of everything. However, it's the complete opposite when you substitute motorcycling for alcohol and drugs. "Crotch-rocket" or "cruiser," the rider is in control of the accelerating "high."

The bike makes you feel in control, and that's extremely exciting and empowering. And, once a recoveree decides to pick-up riding as a substitute, he has acquired a new skill. Then, after some time, the bike becomes an extension of his body. It moves with him, reacting to his every command. Truth-be-told, I feel like a Cyborg when I'm on my iron and steel ride. It is a thrill, but I'm smart enough to know I'm not indestructible.

Do you want to know what's even more empowering? The brotherhood and sisterhood that come attached to being a "rider." For the most part, bikers help each other out. Anytime I pull over on the side of the road for a problem or just stretch my legs, other bikers stop and ask me if I am ok – now, this doesn't happen with most drivers. A recoveree can be a lone wolf or social butterfly, and most bikers won't discriminate.

Just by riding, you enter a group where the primary thing in common is a wonderful mode of transportation for both the mind and body. The biker community and especially a motorcycle club (MC), is an automatic support system. But, like everything in life, there are some negative aspects associated with motorcycle communities. But *still*, once an addict or recoveree decides to replace drugs and alcohol for motorcycling, he becomes a bonafide "rider."

And, after a while, most riders identify as "bikers." (WARNING!) recoverees must exercise caution when it comes to their precious, hard-fought sobriety because it can get compromised. The truth is most people view "bikers," as rough-looking, dirty, hairy, and burly men, who wear black

---

- ADDICT INSIGHT -

"AS MANY WAYS THERE ARE TO "MESS-UP" IN ADDICTION; THERE ARE JUST AS MANY WAYS TO CLEAN-UP DURING RECOVERY."

---

leather and drink or do drugs, just as much they ride their motorcycles. And, although this vague description may fit some of my "biker brothers," it's this unfair stereotyping that does the most harm.

Truthfully, the "biker culture," in and of itself, is an American counterculture that mirrors the drug counter-culture, including, but not limited to, rebellious behavior, outlaw living, recklessness, and freedom-seeking. However, the problem is not with "bikers" or motorcycle clubs; the real problem is the inaccurate perception of "bikers" and the "biker culture." Unfortunately, most of us perpetuate this stereotype because that's what "biker life" is perceived to be.

And, in some cases, these unflattering stereotypes at-tract addicts. Why? Partly because they view this counter-culture as exciting and partially because it mimics the drug culture. So, if a recoveree is interested in this lifestyle, his PRIMARY status should be "sober addict," and his biker designation should fall under a number behind that. Re-coverees and their "helpers" must understand that not all bikers are addicts, but be cautious about active addicts, who are also bikers.

With A Purpose

There is no way a recoveree will remain "clean" and so-ber without a positive substitution in place to fill the void of her drug of choice. Remember, an addict with a SUD will *always* have an addict-identity because it is ingrained in who they are. For years the addict's primary purpose in life was to obtain drugs, use drugs, obtain more drugs, and then use some more drugs. Finally breaking that cycle is one of the biggest fights of a recoveree's life, so going backward is death. Sobriety is a hard-fought, beautiful thing, but at first, it's a shock to the system for someone new to recovery. Without a replacement, aka a new purpose, you can't just remove the alcohol and/or drugs, because they have been the addict's sole purpose of living for a long time.

This purpose **must** be redirected, and substitution is the best way to do that. Religion can serve as a purpose. Family can serve as a purpose. Health and wealth can serve as purposes. Riding a motorcycle also can serve as a purpose. These new purposes are also new lifestyles. Whatever the purpose, it should be all-encompassing - a passion and a goal. I prevent relapses by having multiple substitutions, all of which serve as motivational purposes.

During my recovery coaching sessions, I teach that as many ways there are to "mess-up" in addiction; there are just as many ways to clean-up during recovery. I use CBT to help recoverees change their thought processes and substitute negative thoughts for more positive ones. A recoveree can combine all the substitutions I suggested, or he can use just one or none of them. He should do whatever is compatible with his new in recovery.

The important thing is to replace the drug of choice with a much better (that's not drug-related or alcohol-related) option. When addicts or recoverees have the right substitutions, they don't have time to salivate over cravings because they are too busy feeding their souls with *real* passions. In other words, they don't have time to stress over triggers because they are too busy thinking of **power movements for improvements**. So, he won't be thinking about using alcohol or drugs, because he'll be focused on his substitutions instead.

Remember, a "sober addict" moves with a purpose. The wasted time given away to "addiction debt" can't be returned; however, with recovery comes new opportunities. Encourage your loved one to savor each moment of his "sober life." Help him identify what his purpose is, so that he can move within that purpose. **FYI:** Usually, a purpose is related to a passion.

But, this passion should **not** be related to your loved one's drugs, alcohol, gambling, etc. It should also be a passion that can replace the vices just listed. I used my passions as my substitutions. I planned it that way. My goal was and *still* is to put twice as much energy in fulfilling my passions, as I did in "using and abusing." I don't have "downtime" because I invest my time in productive purposes that will further my journey as a "sober addict." Thus, a recoveree cannot be idle. An idle mind and hands are a "sober addict's" next relapse reason. **Keep doing – Keep busy - Keep sober.**

CONCLUSION

Back to Life

The real-life "Walking Dead" are all around us in high-definition reality. They are our addicted moms and dads, sisters and brothers, friends, significant others, and co-workers. Dead men and women walking amongst us, not looking for brains to eat, but their next "high," drink or "fix." They are the zombies buzzing around street corners, slumped over at bus stops, sleeping in train stations, and pill-seeking at doctor's offices. Our communities are becoming riddled with walking dead addicts, just like in the zombie television shows and movies.

And, just like in those zombie movies, the disease of addiction is spreading, infecting millions, while draining life and potential from all its victims.

It's that lost and wasted potential that sickens me. Many of the addicts I've encountered are *good* people capable of *good* things. They are some of the smartest, artistic, and resourceful people I've ever met. I know this because the level of manipulation and strategy that goes into drug-seeking behaviors takes a lot of brainpower. When I counsel clients, my mind runs laps thinking of the possibilities that could happen if they placed the same motivation into productive things, as they did in their "use and abuse."

There is no doubt in my mind that I would have reached higher levels of success had it not been for my substance use disorder. I know for a fact that I would have had more money, more brain cells, and fewer regrets. I couldn't achieve all of what I was capable of achieving because I was focused only on drugs and alcohol. Let me reiterate that addiction is all-encompassing. Once it grabbed ahold of me, it put me in a death grip. Then, it stopped me from growing. **The truth is addiction stunts all growth.** An addict can't mature or develop because of it. We know from basic biology that if things don't grow, evolve, and adapt - they die.

Soo much wasted potential and so many years passed without me mentally growing. I was making moves, but only moving backward.

So, if you or someone you love is addicted to a "substance" or diagnosed with a SUD, life is probably not as good as it should be. I hope that I sparked the fuse for you or your loved one's personal battle against the disease of addiction. This is a matter of life-and-death, after all. Remember, an addict belongs to the real-life "Walking Dead." She is gradually decaying right in front of you. I know – I was one of them. And, even now, I find it hard to believe that I'm *still* alive.

What I once thought was living can't compare to the *real* living I'm doing now.

If I could come back to life after being a drunk, drugged-up zombie, then ANYONE can. It's all about gaining control of one's and live it more abundantly. You or your loved one can regain control of your life. It's just a matter of getting to the "Turning Point." The good news is that it usually happens after addicts are forced to face the consequences of their actions. The number one reason why active addicts become "sober addicts" is because of consequences. But, even in sobriety, there will *still* be battles to be fought, because addiction is a life-long war. Prepare yourself because this addiction battle will leave plenty of war wounds.

From the scars on my face to the mountain of "addiction debt" I've collected, this disease has marked its territory on me. Honestly, years of "use and abuse" can leave plenty of lasting side-effects. Now that I'm not altering my mood with substances of abuse, I sometimes experience a blah feeling of grayness, like being stuck between happy and sad, unexcited, and detached. I'm describing one of the lasting effects of addiction. This residual effect is the result of a chemical balance in my brain. So, I don't think I'll ever fully recover from all of the damage I've done to myself, but I'm *still* not giving up, and I damn sure ain't giving in.

Even now, I'm *still* playing catch-up, learning, and doing things I should have done years ago. I'm sure others in recovery can relate to my frustration as I try to be a better version of myself in every way. It's all about life. So, the *real* goal of this book is to help the addicted and their loved ones get back their lives, so that they can get back to living.

A "professional-addict-turned-recoveree" must be able to deal with life on life's terms effectively. The effectiveness is accomplished using the tools provided in this book to help you or your loved one gain the upper hand in the internal conflict with external factors. I've listed various methods for you to use as weapons and tools in your fight against addiction. During the "Phases of Addiction," you **must** use all of the tools in your toolbox to fight back.

1. When in a relationship with an addict, try to "substitute the irreplaceable" and "give a whole lotta love" to him or her.

2. Say "No," say "No" often, and don't take things too personally, so you don't lose too much or gain too much in "addiction debt."

3. Use the A.R.M. (Accept, Redirect Motivate) method to stop "enabling."

4. Help the "professional addict" by doing the following:

    a. Changing or removing negative labels

    b. Holding your addicted loved one accountable

    c. Giving the professional addict an ultimatum

5. Develop and Highlight discrepancies every step of the way

6. Force an addict to face the **consequences** of his or her behavior, because it is the only way he or she will reach the "Turning Point"

7. Perform or have your addicted loved one perform the tasks found on the "Turning Point Dos and Don'ts" checklist every day

8. Remember, to achieve long-term sobriety, a recoveree *must* identify certain *wants* and *needs,* and those *wants* and *needs* must be met

9. "Cold turkey" isn't as difficult as some assume, when using DC Hyden's 3Ds of "Cold Turkey"

3Ds of Cold Turkey

❖ Detox
❖ Detach
❖ Declare

10. Know the reasons for the relapse then use tools like R&R (Recognize & Realize) and constant reminders/constant deterrents

11. Healthy and productive substitutes are saving graces for a "sober addict," so develop a bunch of them

12. Prepare for the worst, but expect the best

Addiction is creating zombies, but often they are the slowing dying kind, not-dead-yet, and *still* savable. We, addicts, know our actions are killing us, and with each "Phase of Addiction" gained, more of our humanity is lost. But, if you're an addict reading this, you already know that your life is the only thing you have left to give. The moment you don't have a problem giving your life away to your addiction is the moment you go from being a "Walking Dead" to just being dead. Period. In this day and age, there is no reason for this to happen - no reason for your life and the potential to be wasted. There is no "rock bottom," but there is a "Turning Point." The road there ain't easy, but nothing worth a damn is.

The End

Acknowledgements

Addiction is very personal and self-serving behavior. As an actively abusing addict, I alienated anyone who was not on a bridge I had already burned.

There were a significant amount of people who tried to help me. Even more, people currently assist me in my recovery, and this book would not have been possible without any of them.

All Praise due, with glory and honor forever to my Higher Power, who saved me when I couldn't save myself.

Words will not articulate my love and appreciation for my daughters Amaya and Lailinda.

I cannot express enough thanks to my siblings, especially my sister Daphney,

Thanks and appreciation are extended to Tanya Onsongo and the Fowler family.

To the friends I still have left, thank you for sticking around during my wild roller coaster ride.

Ms. A.V., you are a true human resource, and your AVP is life-changing, you brought an optimistic balance to my troubled life.

To Dr. R.L. Langham for your expertise and keen editorial eye made an invaluable contribution to this book.

Annette Wood, I appreciate your talent, your artistic vision helped to shape this book.

Special thanks for the gift of knowledge from Mrs. D, Ms. Jobi, and the Resource Training Center staff in Sunset Park section of Brooklyn.

I am grateful for the clinical supervision I received while at Chance for Change outpatient treatment center in NYC fand or the great people at Neighborhood Coalition for Shelter, which operates that clinic.

Thank you to all at New York City Department of Health and Mental Hygiene – the Bureau of Alcohol and Drug Use Prevention, Care, and Treatment especially.

Ms. Connie Pacheco I am appreciative of you and your school Recoveries R Us.

My deep and sincere gratitude are extended to the "Director of Empathy," Ms. Alicia Carrasquillo.

The City of New York is my external motivation for internal stimulation.

Glossary of Terms

AAA: Actively Abusing Addict

AA: Alcoholics Anonymous

CBT: Cognitive Behavioral Therapy

CO: Correction Officer

DOC: Drug of Choice

DTs: Delirium Tremens

DUI: Driving Under Influence

DWI: Driving While Intoxicated

MAT: Medication Assisted Treatment

NN: Narcotics Anonymous

OD: Overdose

OWI: Operating While Intoxicated

PTSD: Post Traumatic Stress Disorder

R&R: Recognize and Realize

RRs: Relapse Reasons

SAMSHA: Substance Abuse Mental Illness

Stages of Change: The Transtheoretical Model by Prochaska and DiClemente initially consisting of five stages – Precontemplation, Contemplation, Preparation, Action, Maintenance

Stages of Grief: 1. Denial/isolation; 2. Anger; 3. Bargaining; 4. Depression; 5. Acceptance. First proposed by Elisabeth Kübler-Ross in *On Death and Dying*.

STD: Sexually Transmitted Disease

SUD: Substance Use Disorder

References

Alcoholics Anonymous (2001). *The big book: The basic text for alcoholics anonymous. New York: AA World Services Inc.*

Martin, B. (2018). In-Depth: Cognitive behavioral therapy. *Psych Central.* Retrieved from https://psychcentral.com/lib/in-depth-cognitive-behavioral-therapy/

Prochaska, J. O., Norcross, J. C., & DiClemente, C. C. (1994). *Changing for good: The revolutionary program that explains the six stages of change and teaches you how to free yourself from bad habits* (1st ed.). New York: William Morrow and Company.

List of Illustrations

Made in the USA
Middletown, DE
15 January 2021